FEATURES

KNITTING

*A Victorian Rag Doll To Make
– And Her Sailor Brother!*

COOKERY

Printed and published in Great Britain by D. C. Thomson & Co., Ltd., Dundee. Glasgow,
London and Manchester. © D. C. Thomson & Co., Ltd., 1984.

THE long red and gold coach lumbered into the square like a tired bumble bee and rolled to a stop in a cloud of gritty dust.

Wedged in the front seat, Jean Masters yawned and stretched her legs, too weary for once to worry what impression she made. Her map told her this was the village of Chaumier, in Northern France.

Behind her the other passengers awoke and the familiar buzz of chatter broke out. A hand came down on her arm and she looked up into Alan Seaton's brown eyes.

"How about something to drink?" He held out his hand to pull her up.

How many times have I heard that, in how many towns, she thought, and immediately felt guilty because Alan had been so kind to her during the trip. She followed him down the coach steps.

The Village Of Stay - Awhile

"Don't leave!" he said. "Stay for the rest of your life!"

The driver touched his cap to them. Beads of sweat clung to his brown forehead. "One hour only, if you please, m'sieur, madame. We have hundred fifty kilometres still to go."

Complete Story by JUDITH PICKARD

An hour, Jean thought, as they walked across the gravelled square. An hour of France left to me, and what shall I do with it?

When they reached the cobbled road, Alan took her elbow. His fingers on her bare skin felt as damp as her own.

Ahead, a row of crumbling eighteenth-century houses borrowed a dozen different colours from the afternoon sunlight — biscuit, apricot and gold, with turquoise and purple for the roof tiles.

The little village street stretched hazily into the distance, shimmering with the heat.

Shading her eyes against the sun, Jean let her breath out in a long, deep sigh.

This was France. The France she had always imagined — the France she had come to see.

Suddenly she wanted to get away, away from Alan, away from her fellow passengers in the bus; away by herself to drink in the peace and the stillness.

"I saw a little cafe just as we came in," Alan was saying. "It isn't far, thank heavens. My feet —"

"Alan —" She hesitated. "Alan — would you mind if I didn't come with you? I mean, I'd like — I'd like to go off on my own, spend my last hour in France by myself. You don't mind, do you?"

5

"Why, of course not!" He studied her flushed face. "I say, you aren't feeling ill, are you?"

"No, no. It's nothing like that —"

"We-ell —" He shrugged and let go of her arm. "If that's how you want it, I'll see you back at the bus then, about three."

Where she could, Jean walked in the shadows, wishing she had thought to bring the wide-brimmed hat she had bought in Paris on the outward journey.

That outward journey, so full of hope and promise, seemed a year ago now.

For the first time, she admitted it to herself, the coach trip idea had not worked out. It had been a cowardly second-best because it was her first time abroad.

A coach tour had seemed to offer company and the security of booked hotels, with no need to struggle over Continental timetables or restaurant menus.

Yet almost the moment they had landed in France, the luxury coach had turned into a prison. The frightening thing was that she seemed to be the only one who felt that way.

Her fellow passengers "oohed" and "aahed" at all the recognised places of interest, and chattered amongst themselves when they considered there was nothing to look at.

But from the start Jean had found herself desperately craning back — at the village they had just passed or the heavenly green of a forest as they sped through it.

Glimpsing the reds and browns, and the peace of the winding rivers, she had wanted, time and time again, to bang on the driver's window and cry — "Stop! Stop!"

WALKING now down the village street, she realised how little time she had left.

Tonight they would be in Calais, tomorrow they would make the short Channel crossing and, in two days, she would be back at the supermarket where she was a supervisor — back with Alison, the schoolteacher friend with whom she shared a flat.

We sit there like a pair of broody hens, Jean thought, pretending we enjoy those high-brow plays, and reading books on modern art. Or trying exotic recipes out of glossy magazines with no-one but ourselves to eat them.

Sometimes she found Alison a strain to keep up with. Just occasionally she longed to do something on impulse — to see an unashamedly "weepy" film, or eat a hamburger in the street.

"Impulses are dangerous," Alison always said. "You know the saying, 'Marry in haste, repent at leisure.' "

Jean always smiled at that. She was moderately proud of her slender figure and striking blonde hair; and a small number of men — those who had managed to get her away from Alison long enough — had seemed to enjoy her company and one or two had even asked her to marry them. But she had never felt really in love.

It was only recently that she had become alive to the fact that most of her contemporaries were married, some of them even with children, whereas she, at twenty-seven years old, was merely marking time.

It was this unease that had made her come abroad alone. Alison had booked for a lecture-school on modern art at an old mansion.

"You'd be much better off coming along with me, Jean," she had said. "These impulses of yours are always dangerous."

And now I repent at leisure, Jean thought ruefully. When Alan first introduced himself on the coach she was pleased to find a friend, but soon he had taken it for granted that they should do everything together.

He didn't understand that she didn't feel that way about him, that she liked to be alone sometimes. Oh, he was nice and kind, but he wanted all of her company, and she was unable to give it.

But now for a few minutes she was alone. She walked, without purpose, wondering what the village had to offer.

"You're clutching at a straw," a voice whispered in her head. "It's far, far too late. Go back to Alan and be grateful."

The river, when she came upon it at the bottom of a steep lane, was unexpected and exciting. She swung herself over a low stone wall and landed on a stretch of bleached pebbles.

Taking off her sandals, she walked gingerly forward and sat close to the water's edge. The stones were warm and not uncomfortable, and she felt pleased with herself for finding the spot.

A stone flew over her head and touched the water not a yard away. It skidded, sending up silver drops, and bounced a dozen times before sinking.

There was a gay laugh from behind her and a small boy appeared, grinning broadly. He was bare footed and a pair of once white plimsolls swung round his neck by their laces.

B ONJOUR, Mademoiselle!"
"And to you," Jean said in French. "That was a good one — show me how you did it."

The boy's grin widened and he bent over, searching for another suitable stone. He had on thin brown shorts and a yellow T-shirt.

"Watch!" He flung his arm back and sent another stone on its way. It skimmed halfway across before it sank. He turned to Jean, his face animated.

"Here's one for you. Try it!"

Her stone hurtled a few feet and hit the water obliquely, sending up a shower of spray.

"Non, non! Curl your finger round. Like this." He came closer to show her.

"Alexandre! Don't bother the lady."

The new voice was deep and commanding. A tall man appeared the way the boy had come; Jean did not need to be told he was the boy's father.

"It's quite all right," she said. "We were just having some fun."

The sun was shining into the man's eyes and Jean was able to observe him without seeming rude. From his face she judged him to be forty, although his hair at the sides was only beginning to shade from black to grey.

Round his eyes were deep, delta-shaped lines, but she could not yet decide whether they were the result of pain or laughter. He was carrying a long, bamboo fishing rod.

"You are English," he stated.

She smiled. "Is it my clothes or my accent?"

"Neither," he said with a quick glance at her cotton suit. "They are both charming."

"No, there is a coachload of English tourists in the square. Alexandre and I know everyone in the village, but we do not know you. Therefore you are English. How is that?" He smiled warmly, showing strong white teeth.

"Papa! I challenge you. Can you beat fourteen bounces?" Alexandre tugged at his father's hand.

He took the boy's hand and led him to the water's edge.

"Let's see," he said, crouching to look for a stone.

Jean watched the pair with interest. The boy was a half-size model of his father and there was an unusual confidence between them.

It was the first time she had spoken to French people other than in shops and restaurants. How little use she had made of her holiday, she thought regretfully, and now it was almost over!

The father had found his stone and now he skimmed it hard and low at the river's silky surface. It touched, touched, touched, an uncountable number of times, and bumped against the far bank.

Alexandre gave a low whistle of admiration, with eyes only for the stone. But Jean, watching the father, saw him slide on the mud with the force of the throw.

He swung his arms wildly, twisted round, and sat down neatly in six inches of water.

Jean started up in dismay. Alexandre's eyes opened wide, then he started to laugh uproariously. Infected by his giggles, she had to laugh, too.

There was no trace of annoyance on the man's face. He was happy to hear his son's laughter and instantly played up to it.

"That will teach me to show off!" He grimaced at Jean.

He got to his feet and the water poured off him.

"Your wife will have something to say about this!" she said, smiling.

The man shot a quick glance at the boy.

"Alexandre, see if there are any fish in the deep pool, will you? Perhaps we shall catch our supper today."

The boy seized on the new idea and hurried off to a spot where the river curved widely.

"But don't you fall in, too!" his father called after him, and turned back to Jean.

"His mother is dead," he said quietly. "It was a long time ago, but I do not like to remind him of it."

Jean kept her eyes on the boy. "Yes, of course," she said. "I'm sorry. But won't you have to go home and get dry?"

He shook his head. "Not on a day like this! No, I will lie here and let the sun do the work. That is, if you do not mind," he added quickly.

She shook her head and he stretched out on a patch of wiry grass beside her.

Continued on page 10

8

OCCUPATIONAL
HAZARDS
My mama says
I wouldn't even
know what they
are because Life is
just one endless
round of doing
as I please,
and as long as cows
are milked
and fish are caught
why should I worry?

MOTTO
If at first you
don't succeed,
pry, pry again.

I LIKE PEOPLE

OOH, there's lots of things I like as well as people 'cos I like milk and fish and playing with string and lots of paper and sleeping and milk and fish and chasing my tail and having a quiet look in cupboards and drawers for milk and fish and soft cushions and being tickled behind the ear and I like — oooh, there's so much I like!

My mama knows everything and she says that when you're my size people watch you do naughty things like climbing net curtains or knocking over vases or keeping telling them how hungry you are for milk and fish, and they laugh and say oh isn't he cute, and when you are my mama's size and age they frown and shout and sometimes even throw things just because you've done the very same things, and my mama says just watch out with people because you never know.

Mama says if I ever meet with a big rough noisy dog I've never to speak to him but it's all right to spit, so I'm hoping I'll meet lots and lots of dogs then I can spit, and I like to spit, only Mama says never spit except when you meet dogs and don't forget to arch your back and look twice your size so that you frighten even an Alsatian, and I'll certainly enjoy trying, but what is an Alsatian anyway?

There's so much I'd love to talk to you about but the trouble is I feel so sleepy 'cos I've had my midday milk and fish and I don't understand why it makes me feel so sleepy, for when I wake up I'll be so hungry for milk and fish which I will cry for and when I get it I'll feel so sleepy, and then I'll wake up all hungry again and, oh dear, I hope Mama is right when she says stop worrying and just enjoy life 'cos I try to.

HOW pleasant and natural this seems, Jean thought, clasping her knees. It's as though my holiday has only just begun.

It was hard to believe that within minutes she would be whisked back to the greyness of her everyday existence.

Suddenly a very quiet voice inside her whispered: "Why go back?"

"Papa! Quick! The fishing rod!" Alexandre was running urgently towards them. "I can see a big one, all silver. I'm going to catch him!"

When he had scampered off with the fishing tackle, his father rolled on to his back.

"Where do you come from in England?" he asked.

She told him about the work she did and where she lived. Already her French seemed to flow better than at any other time on her holiday.

She even talked a little about Alison, and let out some of her dissatisfaction with her present life. He asked her what she had liked in France, and as she vainly racked her brains to find something to tell him, he sat up, his brow puckered in a frown.

"I think perhaps you have not enjoyed your holiday?"

Jean shrugged. "No," she said helplessly.

"That is one of the dangers of travelling too fast," he said gravely. "You think you are seeing the world, but, in fact, you are only seeing it at long distance. Like looking through the wrong end of a telescope.

"Here, for a few moments, you are looking through a microscope. You are much nearer to life."

"I know," she said slowly. "I shall be very sorry to go."

"Then why go?" His words were an echo of her earlier thought. She shut her eyes and waited in the concealing golden darkness for him to go on.

"You could get a job — even in this village. I know the priest is looking for a housekeeper, for example."

He spoke lightly, but she felt that he was testing her, testing how much of what she said she meant. Panic rose inside her.

"Oh — I don't know —"

A repeated sound beat on the summer air. Once, twice, a third time. It came from far away and was pitched only a little above the insect hum and the noise of the water. The third stroke had died away before she realised what it was.

"Three o'clock! The bus leaves at three!"

She jumped to her feet and the man followed her back to the street. He held out his hand. "I have enjoyed our talk."

His eyes were humorous, but there was a wistfulness behind them. "Perhaps you will come to Chaumier again some time?"

Jean gave him a tremulous smile. "I'm glad your clothes are almost dry. Thank you for listening to me."

She held out her hand and was surprised when he lifted it formally to his lips.

"Goodbye," she said quickly.

"Goodbye, Alexandre!" she called. In the distance the boy briefly took one hand from his rod to wave.

She ran all the way up the cobbled lane, slipping and stumbling. If the bus goes without me, she thought, my problem will be solved.

But when she reached the square the bus was still there.

SHE was the last to arrive and there was a lot of tongue clicking from the other passengers.

She glared down the aisle at them and flopped back into the front seat beside Alan.

The driver slid the passenger door shut and walked round the front of the coach to his cab.

"Well, how did it go?" Alan asked.

"Fine!" she gasped. "I — I enjoyed it thoroughly."

Sitting limply in her seat, she stared ahead unseeingly.

This is all a dream, she told herself, as though I'd fallen asleep in my seat and dreamed what I wanted to dream.

You're a coward, she said to herself, you know it wasn't a dream! Stop pretending again, stop hiding from reality.

She could still see the Frenchman's eyes, deep and searching as he questioned her, still hear his gentle, steady voice.

With a sudden sense of shock she realised she didn't even know his name. Alexandre's father — that was all she knew him by.

With a prolonged blare on its horn the coach turned into the main road again and pointed resolutely towards the coast.

Ahead, Jean saw a small grey church with a paved patch leading up to it. At the gate stood a tall, black figure wearing a wide-brimmed hat.

The priest! Was he the one who needed the housekeeper?

As the coach went past she found herself trying to look into his face, to judge what sort of man he was.

Surely even now it wasn't too late to make a decision? She only had to bang on the driver's window, as she had longed to do for the past two weeks, get her suitcase from the compartment at the back . . .

She half stood in her seat and raised her hand to the glass.

"What's the matter?" Alan asked. "Have you left something?"

Her courage suddenly failed her, and she quickly sat down again, unable to prevent a tear from escaping down her cheek. It seemed such an enormous decision to have to make on her own.

Yet wasn't that the decision Alexandre's father had been trying to help her with?

"No, Alan, I've left nothing behind," she said.

But I have, she thought, I've left a part of my heart. Whether she had left it with a French village, or with a tall, brown-eyed Frenchman, or simply with a romantic ideal, didn't matter.

Courage wasn't necessary if you simply acted on impulse. For once she was going to act on impulse and see what happened. If you never tried something, how could you ever know the truth of it?

She stood up — firmly this time — and rapped on the glass.

It took some time to persuade Alan and the driver that she knew what she was doing.

She pecked Alan's cheek and told him she would write. Then she watched him climb reluctantly back into the coach.

She stood in the dusty road and watched till it was out of sight.

Picking up her case, she took a deep breath and started the walk back to the village, her heart singing.

The End.

OH, YOU
··BEAUTIFUL··DOLL

Materials Required. For doll — Of **Lister-Lee Richmond Double-Knitting containing Bri-Nylon,** 6 x 50 gram balls Cream (Pearl Oyster), 2 x 50 gram balls Black, odd lengths of red yarn to work nose and mouth and blue yarn for eyes; a a pair of 3¼ mm (No. 10) knitting needles, stuffing and ribbon for bows. For clothes — 3 x 50 gram balls White, 4 x 50 gram balls Blue, 4 x 50 gram balls in Pink; narrow elastic; 4 buttons and a pair of 3¾ mm (No. 9) needles.

For best results it is essential to use the recommended yarn. If you have difficulty in obtaining the yarn, write direct, enclosing a stamped addressed envelope to the following address for stockists: Lister-Lee Knitting Wools and Yarns, George Lee & Sons Ltd., P.O. Box 37, Whiteoak Mills, Wakefield, Yorkshire WF2 9SF.

Measurements. — Height — approximately 84 cm, *33 inches.*

Tension. — Doll — 6 sts. to 2.5 cm, *1 inch,* worked on 3¼ mm needles with double yarn. Clothes — 7 sts. to 2.5 cm, *1 inch,* worked on 3¾ mm needles with single yarn.

Abbreviations. — St.st. — stocking stitch; P — purl; st.(s) — stitch(es); K — knit; tog. — together; cm — centimetres; y.o.n. — yarn over needle; y.f. — yarn forward; y.r.n. — yarn round needle; Pk — pink; B — blue; p.s.s.o. — pass slipped stitch over.

TO MAKE DOLL
Legs.

Using 3¼ mm needles and cream yarn double, cast on 42 sts. Work in st.st for 12.5 cm, *5 inches,* ending with a purl row.

Work 2 rows purl to form stitching line (knee joint). Continue in st.st. for 4 rows.

5th row. — Decrease 1 st. at each end. Work 9 rows.

Repeat last 10 rows twice more, then 5th row once. (34 sts.)

Continue straight until work measures 25.5 cm. *10 inches,* from beginning, ending with a purl row. Break yarn. Join in double black yarn for boot. K17 sts., place next 17 sts. on a st. holder, working on first 17 sts., purl back.

Next row. — K2 tog., knit to end. Work 9 rows in st.st.

Next row. — K2 tog., knit to end. (15 sts.)

Next row. — Purl.

Next row. — Increase 1 st. at end of row.

Next row. — Purl. Repeat last 2 rows 4 times. (20 sts.)

Next row. — Knit to last 2 sts. knit twice into next st., K1.

Next row. — Purl twice into first st., purl to end. Repeat last 2 rows 4 times. (30 sts.) Work 7 rows.

Next row. — P18, turn, knit back.

Next row. — P16, P2 tog., turn, K2 tog., knit to end.

Next row. — P14, P2 tog., turn, knit back. Cast off.

Join yarn to remaining 12 sts., purl to end.

Next row. — K10, K2 tog.

Why not turn
to page 168 to meet
our rag doll's sailor
"brother"?

13

Next row. — P2 tog., purl to end.
Next row. — Knit.
Next row. — P2 tog., purl to end.
Cast off.

Join yarn to 17 sts. on st. holder and work to correspond with first side reversing shapings.

Make second leg to match.

Arms.

With 3¼ mm needles and cream yarn double, cast on 4 sts. and knit 1 row.

2nd row. — Purl, increase 1 st. at each end. Continue in st.st., increase 1 st. at each end of every row until there are 30 sts. on the needle.

Continue straight until work measures 10 cm, *4 inches.*

Next row. — K13, K2 tog., K2 tog., K13.

Purl 1 row.

Next row. — K12, K2 tog., K2 tog., K12.

Purl 1 row.

Next row. — K12, K2 tog., K12.

Continue without shaping until work measures 18.5 cm, 7¼ inches, ending with a purl row.

Thumb.

1st row. — K12, pick up loop between sts. and knit into back of it, K1, pick up loop, knit into back of it, knit to end. Work 3 rows.

Repeat these 4 rows twice more, only work 3 sts. then 5 sts. between pick-up loops.

Next row. — As 1st row but work 7 sts. between loops. (33 sts.)

Next row. — P20, turn, K7, turn, P7, turn, K7, then cast off the 7 sts. Join yarn on purl side in middle of row, purl to end. Continue on 26 sts. in st.st. for 3 cm, *1¼ inches.*

Cast off 2 sts. at beginning of the next 2 rows, K2 tog. at each end of next 4 rows. Cast off. Make second arm.

Body.

With 3¼ mm needles and cream yarn double, cast on 39 sts. Work in st.st. for 11 cm, *4½ inches.*

Decrease 1 st. at each end of the next row. Work 3 rows. Decrease 1 st. at each end of the next row. Work 1

row. Increase at each end of the next row. Work 3 rows. Increase each end of the next row. Work straight until body measures 26.5 cm, *10½ inches.*

Shape Shoulders.

Cast off 4 sts. at beginning of next 4 rows. Work 4 rows in st.st.

Next row. — Increase 1 st. at each end.

Next row. — Purl.

Repeat these 2 rows until there are 39 sts. on the needle.

Continue straight for 9 cm, *3½ inches.*

Next row. — K2 tog., K16, sl.1., K2 tog., p.s.s.o., K16, K2 tog.

Next row. — Purl.

Repeat these 2 rows, working 2 sts. less between decrease 3 times more. (23 sts.)

Next row. — K19, turn, P15, turn, K11, turn, P7, turn, knit to end.

Next row. — Purl. Cast off.

Make another body piece the same.

To Make Up.

Press pieces lightly with a dry cloth.

Stitch boot and leg seams, turn to right side. Stuff boot and leg up to stitching line with seam at back, backstitch through line. Now continue to stuff leg to within 1.2 cm, *½ inch,* of top, stitch cast-on edges together. Stitch thumb and arm seams, turn to right side. Stuff hand flat for 4 cm, *1½ inches,* then stitch three lines to indicate fingers. Stuff remainder of arm. Stitch cast-on edges together.

Stitch sides of body and head together, leaving a space to insert arms and leaving top open. Turn to right side. Attach arms and legs to body.

Stuff body and head firmly. Work face as in photograph, using black yarn for the outline of the eyes and lashes, blue for the pupils and red for the lips and nose.

Using black yarn, attach hair, stitch in the middle decreases of the head to indicate parting as follows: cut lengths of yarn 76 cm, *30 inches,* and taking about 3 strands together, fold in half, stitch at centre point to head, continuing down to nape of neck. Tie in two bunches with ribbon.

DRESS
Back.

With 3¾ mm needles and single Pk yarn, cast on 120 sts.

Border Pattern. — **K2 rows garter st. (every row knit).

3rd row. — K1, *y.o.n., K2 tog., K2, repeat from * to last 3 sts., y.o.n., K2 tog., K1.

4th row. — Knit.

5th row. — K3, *y.o.n., K2 tog., K2, repeat from * to last 5 sts., y.o.n., K2 tog., K3.

6th row. — Knit.

7th and 8th rows. — As 3rd and 4th rows**, making 1 st. at the end of the last row. (121 sts.)

Main pattern:

1st row. — With Pk, knit.

2nd row. — With Pk, purl.

3rd row. — Join in B, K1, *K3, sl.1, repeat from * to last 4 sts., K4.

4th row. — With B, P1, *P3, sl.1, repeat from * to last 4 sts., P4.

5th and 6th rows. — In Pk, as 1st and 2nd rows.

7th row. — With B, K2, *sl.1, K3, repeat from * to last 3 sts., sl.1, K2.

8th row. — With B, P2, sl.1, P3, repeat from * to last 3 sts., sl.1, P2.

These 8 rows form pattern, repeat until work measures 35.5 cm, *14 inches,* from beginning, ending with a wrong-side 4th or 8th row.***

Bodice.

Next row. — In Pk, K3 tog. 15 times, K2 tog. 6 times, K1, slip remaining sts. on to a st. holder, turn, purl back.

Working on these 22 sts., continue in pattern, beginning *K3, sl.1, repeat from *, ending with K2.

Keeping pattern as set, work 9 more rows.

Shape Armhole.

Cast off 3 sts., pattern to end.

Next row. — Pattern.

Continue on these 19 sts. in pattern for 27 rows, ending at centre edge.

Shape Neck.

Cast off 11 sts., pattern to end.

Shape Shoulder.

Cast off 4 sts., pattern to end.

Work 1 row then cast off remaining sts.

Return to sts. on st. holder and join in Pk yarn on right side, K5 sts., then work on these 5 sts. in garter st. as follows:

Knit 7 rows.

*8th row. — K1, cast off 2 sts., K2.

9th row. — K2, cast on 2 sts., K1. Work 10 rows.* Repeat from * to * twice more then 8th and 9th rows again (4 buttonholes).

Knit 2 rows. Cast off.

Stitch buttonband to bodice.

With Pk, cast on 5 sts., knit these 5 sts., then on to the same needle, work the remaining sts. on st. holder as follows:

K1, *K2 tog. 6 times, K3 tog. 15 times. (27 sts.)

Next row. — In Pk, pattern to last 5 sts., K5.

Next row. — K5 Pk, join in B and begin pattern with K3, sl.1.

Next row. — Pattern to last 5 sts., knit in Pk.

Working 5 Pk sts. in garter st. for buttonband, continue in pattern to match right bodice, reversing shapings.

Front.

With 3¾ mm needles and Pk, cast on 140 sts. Work as given for Back to ***.

Bodice.

Next row. — K3 tog. 47 times. (47 sts.)

Next row. — Purl.

Working on these 47 sts., continue in pattern, beginning *K3, sl.1, repeat from * to last 3 sts., K3. Work 9 more rows.

Shape Armholes.

Cast off 3 sts. at the beginning of the next 2 rows.

Continue in pattern for 24 rows.

Next row. — K13, turn, P2 tog., purl to end.

Next row. — Pattern to last 2 sts., K2 tog., turn, P2 tog., pattern to end.

Repeat last 2 rows once.

Continued on page 17

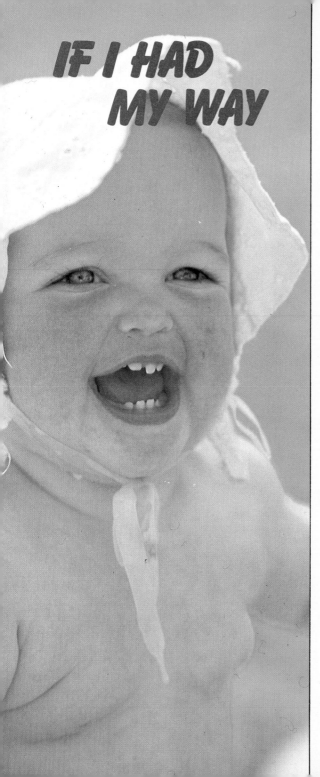

IF I HAD MY WAY

DENTISTS? who needs dentists? If I had my way, I'd have them all conscripted into work of national importance. Like stepping up the production of bigger and better teddy bears. Like louder noises and more colourful rattles.

Oh, I admit I do have teeth. Well, some anyway. But how many do you need to drink milk?

Think of the money I save! Think of the money you grown-ups waste on toothbrushes, toothpaste and all that make-your-mouth-sparkle jazz! All those factories, all that man-power, going to sheer waste, when they could be making more toys and other essentials for people like me.

You're a selfish lot.

I've noticed this grown-up, "what-we-want-we'll-have" attitude in other things. Like a little quiet, for example. Why do you grown-ups want peace and quiet so much? I never hear any of you having a good old gurgling song session in the small hours of the morning.

And when you get annoyed, you go all black as thunder round the eyes. But you don't cry. Not like me. Boy, can I cry! I can wail, moan, sob, girn and howl with the best of them! Why are you grown-ups so mean with your tears?

Mind you, I don't like to see you smile all that much either. You've no idea how horrible you look! All those great big teeth — ugh!

Shape Shoulder.

Cast off 4 sts., pattern 4, turn, pattern to armhole edge. Cast off remaining 4 sts.

Join yarn to remaining sts., cast off 15 for neck edge, pattern to end. Work on these sts. to match right side, reversing shapings.

Sleeves (Both Alike).

With 3¾ mm needles and Pk, cast on 56 sts. Work from ** to ** on dress Back. Knit 2 rows.

Next row (for wrist elastic). — K1, *y.o.n., K2 tog., repeat from * to last st., K1.

Next row. — Knit, making 1 st. at end of row. (57 sts.)

Now work in main dress pattern until work measures 20 cm, *8 inches,* from beginning.

Shape Top.

Cast off 3 sts. at beginning of next 2 rows.

Next row. — K2 tog. at each end.
Next row. — Purl. Repeat last 2 rows twice. (45 sts.)

Next row. — K10, K3 tog. 4 times, K1, K3 tog. 4 times, K10.

Next row. — Purl. Cast off.

To Make Up.

Join shoulder seams then set in sleeves. Stitch side and sleeve seams. Stitch underflap at foot of back opening. Sew on buttons to match buttonholes. Thread elastic through wrist holes.

Neckband.

With 3¾ mm needles and Pk, pick up and K64 sts. round neck edge. Knit 1 row.

Work border pattern from 3rd to 8th row. Cast off.

HAT

With 3¾ mm needles and Pk, cast on 42 sts.

*1st and 2nd rows. — K10, y.o.n., K2 tog., turn, sl.1, knit to end.

3rd row. — K10, y.o.n., K2 tog., K2, turn, sl.1, knit to end.

Repeat last 2 rows, knitting 2 more sts. each time until 4 sts. remain on left needle.

Next row. — Keeping brim and elastic holes as set, K39 sts., turn, work to end.

Work 1 more st. each time until all sts. have been knitted, knit back.*

Repeat from * to * 8 more times. Cast off, leaving a long length of yarn.

Lace Underbrim.

With 3¾ mm needles and white, cast on 7 sts.

1st row. — K2, y.f., K5. (8 sts.)

2nd row. — K4, y.f., sl.1, K1, p.s.s.o., K2.

3rd row. — K2, y.f., sl.1, K1, p.s.s.o., K2, y.r.n. 3 times (3 sts. increase), K2. (11 sts.)

4th row. — K2, K1 into first y.r.n., purl into 2nd y.r.n., K1 into back of 3rd y.r.n., K2, y.f., sl.1, K1, p.s.s.o., K2.

5th row. — K2, y.f., sl.1, K1, p.s.s.o., K7.

6th row. — K7, y.f., sl.1, K1, p.s.s.o., K2.

7th row. — As 5th row.

8th row. — Cast off 3 sts., knit next 3 sts., y.f., sl.1, K1, p.s.s.o., K2. (8 sts.)

Repeat rows 3 to 8 until underbrim is the same length as hat brim.

To Make Up.

With length of yarn draw up crown to a neat circle, then stitch seam. Sew underbrim to hat just below elastic holes, then catch-stitch just above large holes on edging. Thread elastic through holes in hat.

APRON

With 3¾ mm needles and white, cast on 162 sts. Knit 5 rows in garter st.

1st row. — K9, *(P2 tog.) 3 times, (P1, y.r.n.) 6 times, (P2 tog.) 3 times, repeat from * to last 9 sts., knit.

2nd row. — K9, purl to last 9 sts., K9.

3rd row. — Knit.

4th row. — As 2nd row.

Repeat these 4 rows for 32 cm, *12½ inches,* ending with a wrong-side row.

Next row. — K6, K3 tog. 50 times, K6.

Next 2 rows. — Cast on 70 sts., knit the row.

Knit 8 rows.

Cast off 86 sts., knit to end.

Next row (right side). — Cast off 86 sts., K6, (P2 tog.) 3 times. *(P1, y.o.n.) 6 times, (P2 tog.) 3 times, K6.

Keeping pattern correct, work 7 cm, *2½ inches*, ending with a wrong-side row. Knit 4 rows.

Next row. — K6, cast off 18, K6.

Continue in garter st. on these 6 sts. until strap measures 14 cm, *5½ inches*. Cast off.

Rejoin yarn to remaining 6 sts. and work 14 cm, *5½ inches,* in garter st. Cast off. Stitch straps at back of apron.

BLOOMERS

With 3¾ mm needles and white, cast on 96 sts.

1st row. — P2 tog., y.r.n., *(P1, y.r.n.) twice, P2 tog. twice, repeat from * to last 4 sts., P1, y.r.n., P1, P2 tog.

2nd row. — Purl.

Repeat last 2 rows twice more, making 1 st. at the end of the last row. (97 sts.) Break off white.

7th row. — Join in B and K2, *y.f., K2 tog., K2, repeat from * to last 3 sts., y.f., K2 tog., K1.

8th row. — Purl.

***9th row. — Join in Pk, K1Pk, *3B, 1Pk, repeat from * to end.

With B work 4 rows in st.st., beginning with purl row.

Next row. — P2B, *1Pk, 3B, repeat from * to last 3 sts., 1Pk, 2B.

Work 4 rows in st.st., beginning with a knit row.***

Repeat from *** to *** for pattern until work measures 23 cm, *9 inches.*

Keeping pattern correct, shape as follows:

K2 tog. at beginning and end of next and every alternate row until 63 sts. remain. Break off Pk.

Next row. — K2 tog., K1, *P2, K2, repeat from * to end.

Work 3 rows K2, P2 rib.

Next row. — K2, *K2 tog., y.o.n., K2, repeat from * to end.

Work 3 more rib rows as before. Cast off.

Work second half the same.

Stitch legs to crotch shaping, then stitch front and back seams. Thread elastic through holes at legs and waist.

"Please to give m

BY the way, Mum," my son said quite casually, enjoying his third helping of apple crumble and cream. "By the way — I think I ought to tell you I've put down to have one of the German exchange chaps for c term. From Munich. Sounds c smashing sort of lad — name o Heinz. That's his first name."

"You what?" I shouted, and some thing in my ringing tone made hi miss a chew.

I thought, I hoped, my ears ha deceived me. We'd had all sorts

Posed by model.

e construction of your Rolling Poll!"

When I was told Heinzie was coming to stay with us, I felt like weeping, says Joan Wells. And I actually did when the time came for him to go home . . .

y in our house, from old Service
s of my husband suddenly turning
, to hitch-hikers brought in from
e cold by my sons.

So far though, they'd all spoken my
nguage. They had been just men,
oys, and I'd known if I cooked
nough sausages and chips they'd be
happy.

As is my son's way, Richard had
made the tentative arrangements
and consulted me afterwards. This
was because matters always worked
out better without so many tedious
and Mum-like arguments that really
wasted so much time, seeing as Mum
always gave in finally.

Heinz was coming. A German lad
of my son's own age. For three
months.

"But I don't know anything about
German people, what they eat, what
they're used to," I moaned. "He'll
have to share your room and he might
not like that. He may not like our food
— the way we live! I don't know any
German except Donner and Blitzen
and what use are they in a crisis?"

"Now don't flap, Mum," my son

said grandly. "Not a worry in the
world! My German is quite fair and
will be super by the time old Heinzie
goes back. As for food — well, he's
in luck coming here. You just serve
up the usual marvellous stuff and he'll
love it."

The kindly letter I received from
Heinz's Oma — his beloved grand-
mother — didn't make me feel
much happier. It was a long,
splendid missive, in clear, old-
fashioned writing and quaint
English and all about her dear grandson.

His father was dead and his
mother was, for some reason,
ensnared in the Eastern zone, and
Heinz saw her only rarely. Heinz
depended on his Oma for everything,
she prayed that I too would care for
him and see that he came to no harm
during his stay.

He was a good boy and she had
instructed him to obey my wishes
and be of every service to me. I was
to report instantly to her if he didn't
do this.

SUDDENLY it was Der Tag.
We all went off to the station to
meet our guest and there he
stood, the little ribbon "To aid the
looking" in his buttonhole as
promised.

As if I needed it! He stood there,
so forlorn looking, smaller than I'd
expected, in his foreign-looking raincoat, his lovely leather luggage by his
side.

He beamed at us as we introduced
ourselves, his blue eyes alight behind
rimless glasses. He made me a neat
little bow from the waist which
floored me and made the men stare.

In the very first hour back at home,

19

I realised I didn't have to worry about trying to please Heinz.

Everything in our very ordinary house was Very Fine to him. The rooms, the garden — real trees in it! — and even the dog and cat. Living in a flat in the centre of a large town, our small, separate houses, each with its own garden, delighted him.

He was so glad to share Richard's room — "Such an Aid to the Conversation!" He would fill his little books, all ready for new phrases, many times!

His delight too when he saw the television set was touching — for he hadn't one, had rarely watched it at all, and even the blank screen filled him with joy.

When we switched on and the children's programmes began, Heinz hung over the set, utterly thrilled, watching and listening till the news, and then only his natural politeness drew him away for the evening meal.

That was the most unbelievable thing to me about him — his courtesy. It was almost alarming at times, as I wasn't quite used to men leaping up whenever I appeared in the room, grabbing the lightest burdens from me and never, never, sitting down till I was seated!

I was afraid the men would pull his leg, but they held back. Mind you, they didn't attempt to imitate him — it seemed there were limits!

Heinz suffered really badly if I left to get supper while a good television play was on. He, who could only just follow the plot himself in the strange language, would post himself at the dividing doors and give a running commentary on the show.

"Ah! Man enters room. Has gun," and so on. It was so very kind and certainly no-one had ever thought anything of me missing bits of plays before!

As for the food, Heinz loved it. He didn't go much on porridge, which we had each day, but even this he

was courageously prepared to tackle.

"I eat British food," he said valiantly. "Even this porridge, which they say is so very strange. You give me this — I will eat!"

But he liked cornflakes better. He was especially keen on bacon and eggs. He would wipe his plate clean and sigh with content as his glasses steamed up.

He truly liked everything and ate double helpings, treble sometimes, which caused Richard, a redoubtable trencherman himself, to gaze at his guest in deep admiration.

"Good old Heinzie!" he would say proudly. "You aren't very big, but you do appreciate good food!"

"I will become very stout, and my dear Oma will rejoice," Heinz said happily, looking at the huge roly-poly gold syrup pudding one day.

He adore puddings, the gooier the better.

"These so Fine Rolling-Polls, these so fine Puddinks — I would wish you so much to write their construction down for my Oma to follow."

I have often wondered if anyone ever Constructed a Rolling-Poll for dear old Heinz.

I can't think why, but he would never let me wash his socks — he said this was dreadful. I did socks for everyone, every day, and all Heinz's other wash, but right till the end he washed out his own socks and I never solved the mystery.

HE became part of our family quickly, a lonely boy who fitted in right from the start. Very domesticated, he adored helping me in the kitchen "constructing" dishes and was the most entertaining of companions.

He was also a true sportsman and joined in the roughest of rugby games at school. The most tedious of paperchases and cross-country runs saw Heinz always there, always at the rear, but always beaming happily.

He was very popular in class and was invited out everywhere. He grew very brown and cheeky in a gentle sort of way, blossoming to keep his end up completely.

For a start he could lick all our family with one hand tied when it came to things like crossword puzzles, even English ones. He was also a dedicated homework doer and a vast influence for the good on our son.

When the end of his stay came at last, Heinz said goodbye to me the night before. The other men had all gone to a special match of some sort, but Heinz had said he must stay home and "Make Ready" for his journey.

But as soon as I sat down with my mending, he came and sat beside me. He couldn't say a proper goodbye on the station next day as he had learned it wasn't done to show one's feelings in public. He didn't want the chaps to think him soppy.

"But . . ." he said, tears already in his blue eyes. "I am not so steady, not so calm even now and I find it so hard to say farewell to my other mother. But, if I may, I will be your third son and I will work very hard and make you proud.

"And one day, if you will permit it, I will come again and find you all. The little dog, the little Moggy, the blackbirds in the lilac tree who are such friends with us, Robert and Richard and the so-kind Mrs Wells."

I couldn't help having a little weep, too, he was such a nice chap and then I went to prepare our last supper, Heinz assuring me, as usual, that he would be "available" the moment I needed him.

Life wasn't quite the same for quite a while after he'd gone. I don't think any of us will forget our German guest.

The End.

WHAT OUR READERS SAID ON MARRIAGE . . .

I overheard my husband giving advice to our son, aged 14. "Work hard at school. Study all you can now, because soon your thoughts will turn to girls. Have a really good time, but choose glamorous girls to date. Go places and enjoy yourself, but warn them at the beginning that it's only friendship."

He continued: "But when the time comes for choosing a wife, choose a plain girl like your mum. That's the kind who will make you happy, look after your home and love and care for your children. That's just what I did and we are happy."

One evening a girlfriend and I were walking leisurely along a main thoroughfare in Manchester. We passed two boys and I noticed they stopped about 20 yards down the road. We stopped, too.

Then I saw one of them toss a coin into the air. The result — well, I've been married for 42 years to that boy.

And we still toss a coin when we're in doubt!

I saw a woman struggling to get a large, heavy suitcase into the back of a taxi while the driver sat puffing away at a cigarette.

"Come on," he was saying. "I've got work to do after I've run you home!"

So that was it — she was his wife!

THE whole village was agog when the news got about that old Mr Garrett's cottage had been sold at last.

Nobody had lived in it for so long we had begun to think it would stand empty and derelict until it eventually crumbled to dust.

But now a big notice-board had been stuck in the front garden.

SOLD by F. Willey, High Street, Marden, it said.

Marden is our nearest town, where we go to the market every Thursday, buy our clothes and see films that are usually not more than three years old. Marden, in fact, is our contact with the outside world.

Everybody was wondering who could have bought the cottage.

It would be a "foreigner," of course. We knew that without being told. Nobody in our neighbourhood would have had it as a gift.

It might be picturesque, with its jasmine under the window and the clematis thick about the porch, but we believe in being up to date in Lawley. Modern kitchens and bathrooms we must have, and Mr

The Secret Life Of Mrs Williams

— whose love stayed steadfastly through all the whispers and head-shaking.

Garrett's were practically museum pieces they were so ancient.

At last tradesmen came out from Marden and began mending and papering and painting. And, as soon as they'd gone, Mrs Perkins, whose daughter works in the Marden solicitor's office, came to scrub the whole cottage.

You would never believe the number of women who found they had something urgent to say to Mrs Perkins that day.

They popped in to ask about the Women's Institute meeting and how her old mother was, and would she be going to the choir trip and any other excuse they could think up.

Some didn't even bother about an excuse. They just called.

By midday the entire population knew that Copse End had been bought by an elderly lady named Mrs Williams, who was coming from "somewhere beyond Olford."

She was a widow, evidently, for she was coming alone.

This was, in a way, fairly satisfactory, though Granny Beavers thought Mrs Perkins could have found out a good deal more if she'd had any gumption — her Mavis being in Jackson & Deans' office.

Granny, of course, is an expert at knowing about everybody. And what she can't find out for herself, she asks.

Two days later the furniture came, and Fred Beavers got word to meet the evening train with his old Ford.

Luckily it was a fine warm evening, so everybody could get ahead with setting their front gardens to rights — and just happening to get a good view of our new neighbour when she arrived.

Rather disappointed a few of them were, for Mrs Williams was a very ordinary, grey-haired, dumpy little woman, who didn't look as if she'd have a great deal to say.

Still, in a small place like Lawley anybody new is a great event, so we reserved judgment as we watched her pay Fred and go in and close her front door.

WE knew, of course, she'd be bound to go in to Mrs Gates at the shop next morning, and so she did.

One or two had meant to go shopping that morning, too, but Granny Beavers beat them to it.

She had her hat on and her handbag and basket in her hand, and was watching from her window by nine o'clock.

When she saw Mrs Williams coming down her garden path, she popped out and just happened to be going out of the gate as she passed.

Of course she passed the time of day, and Mrs Williams said, yes, it was a lovely morning and it indeed made you feel glad to be alive, and they walked along to the shop together.

A regular old butter-tongue is Granny Beavers, so she soon learned that Mrs Williams had taken the cottage when she was left on her own, because it was small and easily run. Yes, she said, she'd be living there all by herself.

Complete Story by G. E. GRAHAM

"But have you no children to visit you, then, Mrs Williams?" Granny said, never being one to miss anything for the want of asking.

Mrs Williams looked at her in a funny kind of way, as if she was thinking something out, and then she said that she had just the one son and he was very tied by his work and couldn't get away often.

Then Granny told Mrs Williams about all her family, down to the last great-grandchild, and Mrs Williams thawed out and got really friendly and offered her a knitting pattern for her granddaughter.

She said she hoped to see the children soon, so Granny took her to call on the way home.

When we saw that, we knew she was all right and a sociable sort.

We were quite right, too. By the time she'd been in the village a month we felt as though she'd always been there.

She was always ready to baby-sit for the young marrieds. They were always calling in to chat to her, to tell her their little problems, and to listen to her advice.

The children came calling on her as well. They'd knock at her door with bunches of wild flowers or bags full of mushrooms. You never saw her without two or three of them with her. They all made straight for Mrs Williams, like bees for a honey jar.

All that month we saw no sign of her son visiting, though she got letters from Olford regularly, and we supposed they came from him.

She'd told us a bit about him by then, of course, and we knew he was in a good job in Olford. He wasn't married yet, though she hoped he would soon be, as he was over 30.

ONE day Granny showed her their old album with all the family photos, and asked if she had one of her son she could show her.

Next time Granny called, Mrs Williams had a photograph all laid out ready.

A real handsome man he was, tall and fair, with a smile at the corners of his mouth, and a twinkle in his eyes.

Granny said if he'd been her son, she'd have got an enlargement made of that photo and set it up where everybody could see it.

Mrs Williams thought that was a good idea and, next market day, she went into Marden and called at the photographers to see about it.

She got it the following week. She set it on the mantelpiece in her little parlour, and entertained all her visitors in there so they could admire it.

Everybody agreed she had reason to be proud of such a fine-looking son.

After a while, some of the gossipy ones began to talk about his never coming down to see her. After all, they said, he must have some time off.

One or two thought he must be courting in Olford, but the others soon told them that if he was, it was high time he brought the girl to meet his mother.

Whether Mrs Williams heard any of this talk we never knew. But soon afterwards she got a letter and told us James was coming for the week-end.

She cleaned every corner of the cottage and had a big baking day — both cakes and pastry — and had everything just so for the occasion.

Of course we were all real pleased he was coming to see his mother. "And not before time," some said acidly.

Then, after all her preparations, he didn't come.

She got a letter on the Saturday morning, and, after she had read it, she went round the village and invited all the youngsters to come to tea with her.

Her son had been taken ill with flu, she said, and wouldn't be able to come this weekend after all. And she couldn't possibly eat all those cakes and things herself, she explained.

She smiled and looked so happy to have the children, but we knew she must be real disappointed and we felt sorry for her.

Still it couldn't be helped, we said, and there would be another weekend soon when he would come.

A fortnight after that, at the Women's Institute meeting, she told us her son had got engaged.

He'd been going with a girl in Olford for quite a while, it appeared, but she wouldn't make up her mind.

Mrs Williams thought she must have relented when he was ill, and now they were engaged. She hoped they'd get married soon.

We felt she was thinking of the time when she would have her own grandchildren to give sweets to and to go skipping around her when she went on her walks.

We knew she loved the youngsters in the village; but, say what you like, your own kin are different.

AFTER that we kept getting news about them, though they didn't get the wedding fixed very fast.

When our children decided to get married, they get married and no playing around for two or three years till they can afford this and that, and the other. Perhaps they're slower about these things in the towns.

Mrs Williams seemed quite content about it. She knew the girl and liked her, so that was all right.

She brought snapshots along to the meetings to show us and a real pretty girl her James had chosen — as fair as himself and tall, too, like him. We'd expected a brunette, somehow.

It must have been nearly a year after Mrs Williams came, that we heard her James was going to be married in the spring.

Well, we thought, now we'd surely see them both. He would be bringing her through to visit his mother. One or two even hinted as much to her, but she said he couldn't get away.

By that time there were quite a few beginning to think he wasn't as good a son to her as he might have been. Olford isn't so very far away, and a year is a long time.

Still, it wasn't really any of our business, so we didn't say much, even among ourselves. Except for the gossipy ones. They said what we all thought — and you can't help thinking, can you?

Mrs Williams herself seemed quite happy, just getting the letters.

She was friendly with all the village by then and everybody liked her — even old Roger Wilkes, who's about as surly an old chap as you could meet anywhere.

Often we'd see him of an evening, pottering in her garden.

"HEY, THAT'S ME!"

My seven-year-old son arrived home from school earlier than usual. Since I normally meet him, I asked him how he got across the busy street.

"It's all right, Mummy," he said. "God told me when to cross."

Thankful that he was home safely, I smiled and didn't pursue the subject any further.

Next day a neighbour explained the mystery.

My son had been standing at the zebra crossing with cars flying past, when a police car pulled up, stopping the traffic. A voice from its loudspeaker boomed out: "The little boy in the blue blazer can cross."

If anyone mentioned it to him, he'd just growl and say digging was no kind of job for a woman. Though we'd never noticed him helping out anywhere else.

About October some of the more outspoken ones asked her when we were going to see her James and his girl.

They pretended to make a joke of it and laughed a bit, and said they were beginning to think we never would see him.

Mrs Williams just smiled her quiet smile and said he would come when he could — maybe he'd manage at Christmas.

At the end of November she got a letter, and that really was something.

It appeared James had got the chance of a marvellous job in Australia. He was going to be married straightaway, and he and his wife were to sail early in the New Year.

Mrs Williams went into Marden and had her hair waved, and bought herself new clothes for the wedding.

We all went along to see them when they came and they were real smart and pretty.

The dress was a deep pinky shade, and there was a black coat and a little black hat with feathers exaclty the same pink as the dress.

We guessed she'd paid a pretty penny for all that, not to mention the new shoes and handbag and gloves she'd got, too.

She went to the station in Fred's new car, the one he got when the old Ford finally broke down.

We stood at our gates and waved her off. She looked just like a bride herself, smiling and waving as she passed.

We were glad she was so happy about the wedding, but we meant to make her specially welcome when she came back, for we knew she would feel it.

Australia is an awfully long way away, and Mrs Williams wasn't so young any more. Perhaps she wouldn't see her James again. We were glad our lads were content to stay near home and work on the farms and such like.

MRS WILLIAMS was away more than three weeks. We all got cards from her at Christmas and the children got little gifts.

We were real mad we hadn't thought to get her address, but we'd imagined she'd be back to spend Christmas at Lawley with us.

The New Year was a week old when she came back. She looked tired, but she smiled and waved, and looked real pleased to see us all again.

Mrs Perkins had been in to dust the cottage, so that gave us our chance and we all sent something in for her.

Some made cakes and others sent pots of their own preserves or jars of fruit they'd bottled in the season.

The youngsters had made her presents — knitted tea-cosies and coal gloves, and egg racks, and shoe shine boxes they'd made at the woodwork class and such like.

Mrs Perkins had stayed to get her tea ready so she could have it as soon as she got in, and she told us afterwards that Mrs Williams had a little weep when she saw all the things.

She was as cheery as ever next day, though, and came round visiting us all to thank us, and we thanked her for the Christmas things she'd sent us and told her how glad we were to see her back in Lawley.

It was nothing but the honest truth, too. It was surprising how much we had missed her while she was away.

She showed us photos of the wedding, and what a pretty one it had been! A real fairy-tale bride the girl looked in the pictures, with six bridesmaids and two little pages, and Mrs Williams' James made such a handsome bridegroom we nearly forgave him for not coming to Lawley.

Nearly — but not quite.

After that we got news of how he was doing in Australia in his marvellous new job, and there were photos of his wife and him in their new home.

It was obviously a good job he'd got, too, for the house was a real nice one, with a good bit of land to it and they had a big car and riding horses, too.

We began to wonder if Mrs Williams would be going out there beside them. We hoped, for her sake, that she would, and, for ours, that she wouldn't.

You should have seen her face when she showed us the letter that told of their baby son and the pictures of him.

A beautiful child he was — fair like his parents — and lively-looking as well. We only wished Mrs Williams could have had him near to love and cuddle and make much of.

You could see she wished it, too, but she took it out in loving the children who were near at hand, and they loved her dearly in return.

If any of the young mothers missed their youngsters, they could be sure they would find them up at Copse End with Mrs Williams.

It was about then we first noticed she was beginning to fail.

In the autumn she took ill and had to go to bed. We sent for Dr Blake and he came and said she needed to rest, and gave us some medicine for her.

Mrs Perkins went in every morning to clean the house and we all popped along in turns to see her so she wouldn't be left on her own.

I had all mine married by then, and my John's an understanding sort so I took to going along to her cottage to sleep at nights.

I was there the night she died.

I heard her call, and went through, and she was sitting up in bed, looking rather flushed and excited.

I asked her if she wouldn't be better lying down, and she said no — she wanted to tell me something and then I could tell the others and she hoped we wouldn't think too badly of her for what she'd done. And then she told me.

SHE had never been married at all, and she hadn't any son. She had worked all her life as a children's nurse in big houses, going from one family to another as the children grew too big to need a nurse.

After she retired, one of her "boys" had bought her the cottage.

When she first came we'd all called her Mrs Williams, and been kind and interested and had asked about her family and so she had pretended.

She had always longed for children of her own, so she had made up a son.

When Granny Beavers asked to see a photo of him, she showed her one of her favourite charge, who was in Olford and who used to write to her regularly.

The one who had bought her the cottage, he was, and very good he'd always been to her.

Then she gradually slipped into the way of bringing up his news and so we heard of his engagement and saw the pictures of his girl.

They'd invited her to the wedding just like one of the family, and she'd had a lovely time.

She told me where to find his address, and asked me to let him know after she had gone.

"Was it very wrong of me?" she said.

Well, you can guess how I felt and I told her that, of course it wasn't, and to lie down and I'd bring her a hot drink.

So she smiled at me, looking so relieved that she'd got me told, and lay down.

I went to warm some milk and when I came back, I thought she was asleep, but I should have known better.

She was holding something in her hand, and, when I looked, it was his photo, and on the back, in her writing, were the words — "James — My Son."

The End.

"Oono, Dose, Trays y Kwatro!"

NO, that's not a slogan for some foreign convention. It's merely a phonetic impression of the Spanish for "One, two, three and four"!

At the moment Spanish — or rather, the learning of it — is slowly blighting my life.

It all began when two friends told me that they had decided to learn Spanish since they were going to Spain for their holiday this year. They talk Spanish to each other at every opportunity, and to prove to me how much they've learned, talked to each other most fluently.

I was very impressed. But the Man Of The House (ever in search of a "different" holiday) came home the next day, plus as formidable a lot of language text-books as I ever wish to see.

From that day, life has consisted of "Bonno deeas, saynora" (at least that's what it sounds like!) and "Hasta la vista, saynora!"

And this, of course, extends to the meal table. For the life of me, I can never remember the Spanish for "Pass the salt" or "Pass the sugar." But naturally he can.

I'm getting an inferiority complex about the smug way he rattles out his little phrases. If he smiles just once more when I look blank, I'll take an onion to his Spanish bunion or whatever it is one does to shut up a Spanish-speaking moron!

I wouldn't really mind so much — indeed I'd make a serious effort to learn the lingo — if only there was the slightest prospect of getting to see Spain. But what's the use of being able to say "Is this deck-chair taken?" in Spanish — when you're on holiday in Morecambe?

A CHILD CALLED HOPE

**Complete Story
by MURIEL McNAUGHTON**

SAM glanced at his wrist-watch — half past four. He took off his glasses, got up stiffly from the stool in the back shop where he had been working and went to look out through the little bow-fronted window.

Yes — there she was, just as he'd seen her at the same time every day for a week. He watched her as she came running up the cobbles, dark hair flying, her schoolbag swinging from her shoulder.

Now she had stopped outside the window, pressing close against the glass, unaware he was watching.

He saw again the tense, anxious look in her eyes give place to one of relief. He could almost read her thoughts — it was still there — it hadn't been sold . . .

He knew the child had eyes for only one thing among the curios and antiques in his window — a small wooden Madonna and Child on a shelf at the back. He had bought it at a sale a fortnight ago.

The figures were carved in oak with great simplicity, but the expression on the Mother's face as she looked down at the sleeping child in her arms moved him more than he cared to admit.

Not surprising, he thought, that it seemed to have become a kind of talisman to the little girl who now stood gazing at it, her eyes wide, lips parted, showing pearly teeth and a faint colour in her small, pale face.

After a few minutes she drew a deep breath, turned slowly away, and began to walk on down the street.

Sam sighed and went back to the little workroom where he spent so much time polishing and restoring the old silver and furniture which were his stock in trade.

As he worked he decided that the next day he would speak to the child. He found her oddly appealing, reminding him of his own daughter as she had been at the same age.

Yes, he would talk to her, ask her what it was about the little Madonna that attracted her so much.

But the following morning, summoned by the jangling of the bell on his shop door, Sam found the old priest from St Teresa's Church standing at the counter. In his gnarled old hand he held the wooden Madonna.

Sam heart sank. Never before could he remember being unwilling to make a sale — but now he knew he did not want to sell the little statue.

Father O'Madden was beaming at him, his eyes twinkling behind the thick lenses of his glasses. The Madonna, he said, was just what he was looking for, for the new children's chapel at St Teresa's.

The old man noticed Sam's hesitation.

"It's not sold, is it?" he asked. "I do hope not."

"No, no," Sam said unhappily, thinking of the child's stricken face when she came to the shop and found the Madonna gone.

He felt it would be cruel to sell it, almost a betrayal. But business was poor these days, and here was the kindly old priest holding out the money for his purchase.

To refuse him would involve Sam in being either untruthful or discourteous. So he wrapped up the Madonna reluctantly, and Father O'Madden stepped into the street, holding his parcel lovingly.

Sam turned away with a sigh. Without the wooden Madonna, the little shop felt strangely empty.

THAT afternoon he dreaded half-past four, and found himself glancing apprehensively at his watch every few minutes. As the church clock struck the half-hour he saw her, her eyes shining, her face expectant as she sped up the hill.

She stopped outside the window and looked at the shelf.

It was as though a light had been snuffed out.

She drew her breath sharply, the tinge of colour drained from her cheeks, leaving them blanched and waxen. She looked desperately round the shop window, and finally gazed for a long moment at the space on the shelf.

Sam thought she was going to cry, but she turned and walked slowly away down the narrow street, her feet dragging. She did not once look back.

He did not see her again — she must have begun to go home a different way, he thought. He missed her bright, eager face and felt vaguely uneasy, and rather guilty — though he told himself this was ridiculous, and tried to shake the feeling from him.

Several days went by. Sam was bewildered by the feeling of aimlessness and loss which pursued him. He could not dismiss the picture of the child's face as he had last seen it.

Then, late one afternoon, just as he was preparing to close the shop, a thin, harassed-looking man came in, anxiety written on every line of his face. Sam felt there was something familiar about him.

"Excuse me," the stranger began nervously. "I've rather an unusual request."

He paused as though searching for words.

"It's my little girl, Hope. She's only seven years old, and she's very ill with pneumonia. She keeps asking for something she's seen in your shop window, a mother and baby, carved in wood, she says. She talked of nothing else — I don't know why — unless —"

He paused again awkwardly, and then went on, "Well, you see, she lost her mother a year ago — the baby died, too."

Sam had a feeling of overwhelming pity and helplessness.

"I'm terribly sorry," he said. "But, you see, I sold the Madonna last week."

The stranger looked at him uncertainly.

"Oh, well, I'm sorry to have bothered you. I — I don't know what to do now."

Sam watched him go, hesitating only a moment before running after him into the street.

"Don't worry," he said quickly. "I know who bought the Madonna. Please give me your name and address, and I'll try to get it for you."

Ten minutes later he was telling his story to the old priest in church.

"So you see, Father," he finished, "I want you to let me buy back the Madonna."

The old priest shook his head.

"I won't sell it, my son."

Sam's heart sank — but then the priest went on: "I'll take it to the child myself!"

As he handed over the name and address the child's father had given him, Sam was aware of an overwhelming feeling of relief.

Next morning, almost as soon as he had taken down the shutters and unlocked the shop door, he saw the child's father. He came swinging up the hill and Sam noticed that he looked relaxed and confident.

"I've come to thank you," he said simply. "Hope's so much better. She fell asleep almost as soon as Father O'Madden put that wooden Madonna into her hands — and she slept all night. She's so much better — almost a miracle it seems."

Sam watched him as he walked back down the street.

Yes, he thought, and a slow smile lit his lined face. Almost a miracle.

The End.

by CAROLYN WILSON

"WHEN IN ROME...

Do As The Romans Do"

Whoever First Said That Obviously Hadn't Tried It!

THE first day of my long-awaited holiday in Rome.

I was awakened by hot sun streaming into my room. I opened my window and took a deep breath. Wonderful Italian breakfast smells wafted past my nostrils, and I could hardly wait for the gorgeous continental breakfast I'd heard so much about. Thick, strong coffee. Crisp rolls and butter.

What a bitter blow when breakfast was actually served. Corn flakes, followed by a kipper!

Then the owner of the little Italian "pensione" and his wife introduced themselves. Phil and Doris from Hackney.

FOR months before my holiday I had sat in, night after night, with books of Italian phrases and elementary grammar.

So, breakfast over, I stepped out into the bustling, sun-drenched streets, eager to blend with the happy Italian throngs.

My phrase-book was tucked away in my handbag — just in case.

But really, after all my studying, I considered I was able to cope with most situations, whether it was haggling with street vendors over the price of fruit or, with a few apt and cutting remarks, sending amorous Italian men (I'd heard they flocked around women like flies) packing.

At lunch-time I discovered a quaint little restaurant tucked away in a back street. Now was my chance.

I sat down and studied the menu, all ready to give my order in — well, no point in being modest — pretty fluent Italian.

The waiter came. I had just opened my mouth to speak when an elderly lady at the next table leaned over.

"You are Eengleesh? Do permit me to help you order. I was governess in Eengland before de war."

She translated the entire menu for me, ordered for me and chatted with me for a while — in Eenglish.

IT was as I was leisurely sipping a glass of wine at a pavement cafe that I encountered my first amorous Italian.

He was very good looking. I had to admit, and in a way I was flattered by his attention.

He got up and walked towards me.

I began to panic. All the Italian I knew suddenly left me.

He was leaning across to me now, whispering.

"Excusa me, signorina, buta de label of your dress ees hanging adown youra back."

In fact it was only during the last three days of my stay I had a real opportunity to speak Italian — to a young man I met on a bus tour.

Next year I'm going to visit him at his home — in Vienna!

Yes, he's as Austrian as they make 'em. And since the only language we have in common is Italian, all my months of hard study will be put to good use. □

C

Posed by model.

The Wonderful Tramp

Have you ever noticed that some people who haven't two pennies to rub together are among the richest in friends? Scotty was a man like that . . .

by ANNE BUCHANAN

THE first snows had fallen and the mountains and valley were blanketed in white. We put up our storm shutters and set about preparing ourselves for the long, hard Canadian winter.

The money we had worked so hard for through the summer would just about stretch till next spring — if we handled it carefully. And my husband, Frank, was determined we should do just that.

He was quite right, of course, but I think he actually enjoyed scraping the pennies.

By dint of much persuasion I had managed to wring enough out of him and the housekeeping money to get a rather small turkey.

We had mince-pies and Christmas cake, maybe not as rich as some years, but nevertheless a cake. And when I took a look at the jars of fruit and fruit juices I had bottled in the midst of the season of plenty, Christmas began to look a bit cheerier.

Now all that was needed was the tree. Christmas Day was on a Monday that year, and Frank had promised to take the boys out to the woods to cut the tree on the first day of Al's holiday, the Saturday. Unfortunately a heavy blizzard held up the project.

On Sunday I started to stuff the turkey, and was wondering again whether its slender carcase would stretch the distance — when Alistair came rushing in to tell me that someone was coming. Through the window I could see a solitary figure weaving its way towards the house, and even at that distance I knew it was Scotty.

I burst open the door of the sitting-room.

"For heaven's sake," I shouted, "Scotty's coming . . ."

"Scotty? Here? Where — where is he?" Frank raced to the window.

The figure was nearer now: an

34

upright, bronzed man with white, crimply hair, his old coat flapping open in the wind as he walked towards us. He was waving something above his head. I knew what that was also — a bottle! And if his gait was anything to go by, it was by no means full.

"Frank, what are we going to do?"

"Do — do? Get the kettle on, of course . . . it's Scotty!"

"I just said that. But he'll stay . . ."

"Stay? Of course he'll stay — it's Scotty, isn't it?" He looked at me as if I'd taken leave of my senses.

I could have hit him. The turkey was small enough, but now with another mouth to feed . . . I felt a distinct lack of Christmas spirit as my fellow countryman loomed larger than life in the doorway.

With a flourish he banged the bottle on the table — and beamed at us. "And a merry Christmas tae ye all —"

Of course, I softened immediately; it was difficult not to feel kindly towards him, or anyone for that matter, who felt so well disposed towards the whole world.

S COTTY must have been about fifty, not unusually tall nor broad, but he gave the effect of both height and size, for he carried himself erect, head held high.

His accent was totally unaffected, even after twenty years in North America.

By profession he was a landscape gardener, but due to a fondness for the bottle it was now impossible for him to keep a job for any length of time. And so he had become a drifter, coming up to the valley in the early winter, or acting as head cook in a swank Vancouver restaurant. The winters he spent on the "dole," or with the fishing fleet off the coast.

We first met him when we were picking fruit in the orchards.

Most of the pickers were of Indian, Russian, Japanese, Italian, Hungarian or half a dozen other extractions, so even the most casual conversation needed time and effort.

And as Scotty loved to talk, and as we were just about the only ones he could talk to, he latched on to us. Plus the fact that he liked to think himself an exile and was always glad to talk of the Old Country.

So Scotty became a frequent, and most welcome, visitor to the house.

One day Scotty didn't turn up for work and we went to ask the boss where he was. The boss smiled a cynical smile and promptly got into his truck and drove us to the nearest jail.

Sure enough — Scotty was there.

It seemed that when he started to drink, Scotty became another character. His dour, fighting spirit came to the surface. And among the colourful clientele of the taverns and beer parlours of British Columbia it was a simple matter to get involved in a fight.

With Scotty it was a matter of principle — any excuse would do.

No matter what size his opponent was, Scotty would be in there, fighting to exhaustion for his principles, and his principles always landed him in jail.

Of course, we had put up our share of bail in the past.

The last we had seen of Scotty was in the early autumn. He had stayed with us for a day or so on his way to a new job, and I had lent him a few dollars to see him there.

The following day we received a terse phone call from the Mounted Police. Sure enough, Scotty was with them. This time it was 75 dollars bail or three months. With mixed feelings we said we couldn't afford it, and up the river went Scotty.

And so here he was again, "fresh out" of jail and ready to share our Christmas dinner. Obviously he bore us no ill-will for letting him down in one of his many hours of need.

H E and Frank took the bottle and moved into the sitting-room, and I continued with the lunch.

It was a very cheerful meal. The boys loved it when Scotty was there — he could be counted on to keep the conversation away from school and things like that, and he always had a fund of stories, true and otherwise, about the woods, lakes, mountains or towns, all featuring that hero of heroes, Scotty.

The house had really begun to sound like Christmas, and if I hadn't kept thinking about our scrawny little turkey I could have been happy, too.

We love to make our own Christmas decorations, and the room looked lovely with its red stars lining the curtains, silver angels and laurel leaves round the walls. Scotty admired everything with an expert eye and a real sincerity that was typical of him.

Then, addressing the boys, he said solemnly:

"I see ye havna got your tree yet."

All eyes turned towards Frank, who made a few half-hearted attempts to explain the delay, but Scotty heard none of these.

"Boys," he said suddenly, "I'll get ye a tree, a real tree, from floor tae ceiling, the best in the forest. Come on."

The boys lit up with enthusiasm, and within minutes were muffled and ready. Scotty threw an axe and some rope into the truck and started working on her to get her going.

Then all five of us jammed into the truck — and we were off.

The sun glinted on the lake of ice and on the snow-covered mountains that surrounded us, softening the cold, clear air. The snowploughs had cleared the lake shore road, and the going was pleasant and easy; until Scotty indicated that he wanted to turn off on to one of the mountain roads.

I could feel my hair begin to rise.

Frank headed the truck for the slopes with a roar, much to the delight of the boys, and we sped up the first few hundred yards. But the gradient became steeper and the tracks gave out altogether.

The truck showed her disapproval of the whole business by spinning round in the soft snow and coming to a standstill, nose facing firmly downhill. She had my full support.

I was all for turning back to civilisation, warmth and Christmas, with an ordinary, plain, common or garden spruce.

But Scotty was not so easily put off.

"Oh, lassie," he said, "it was a tree I said I'd get ye — not a bush! It's the best we're after, and the best aye grow at the top. I ken this place like the back of ma hand. There's an old logging trail a little way from here . . . now don't worry . . ."

Dragging rope and axe from the truck, he started up the slope, the boys whooping after him. Frank grinned sympathetically.

"You'd rather stay here? I'll leave the engine running for the heater . . ." But the prospect of waiting by myself in the wilderness for a treeing party that might or might not return was not too inviting.

The advance party was already out of sight, lost in the timberland, and all we could see were the tracks, but Frank was enjoying the exertion and in good spirits. We could hear the twins calling to each other, and we hurried to catch up with them.

Being with Scotty had gone to their heads, and they were wild with excitement.

"Here, Scotty, what about this one? Yowee, this is a beaut! Scotty, where's the axe?"

But always the same answer in Scotty's matter-of-fact voice.

"No, laddie, it's the best we're after — the best grow at the top."

"Oh, my golly, they are going to the top." Frank groaned. By this time I had got the giggles and only managed to snort out something about it all being for the best. My sense of humour was not appreciated.

"I ought to have had more sense than to let them go off with a half-soused Scot," he grumbled. "Where the devil has he taken them?"

He left me and strode ahead.

I gave up and sat down on an old tree stump. It was very pleasant in the high woods. The firs and pine trees were beginning to lose their covering of snow, and every now and then a branch would feel its burden slide off and spring back up again in sudden life, shaking neighbouring branches into a flurry of miniature snowstorms.

A sudden crescendo of excitement brought me back to the present as Alistair and Peter came whirling down between the trees in a shower of snowflakes, laughing and shouting that they had found it — their tree.

"Just wait till you see it, Mum," Alistair yelled. "It's enormous! The best in the forest. You should have seen Scotty swinging the axe . . . and the rope . . . we pulled the rope . . . we pulled it down. Scotty said we were natural-born lumberjacks!"

What other feats of strength they had performed were interrupted by the sight of Frank and Scotty coming down the slope, carrying the tree.

Scotty held it upright in front of me and slowly turned it round.

"Well," he demanded, "did I not tell ye I would bring ye the finest tree in the woods?"

For a moment I was speechless; that was no exaggeration, this was the finest tree in the land. From every angle it presented a perfect aspect. Not a bald patch, not a straggling twig marred its sides; thick and green, the remains of a covering of snow still sparkled on its branches — the perfect tree.

We carried it home in triumph, but it was Scotty who stood it in the window corner, Scotty who lovingly arranged the decorations. It was his contribution to our Christmas.

I knew then this was his way of saying, "Thank you." □

SLICK SALES

Having heard so much about slick-talking salesmen, I decided to have a go at the slick patter myself.

When an eager young salesman came to my door enquiring whether he could interest me in a new carpet sweeper, I smiled brightly and replied:

"I'm selling one, too. Care to buy it?"

His months of training deserted him. He just managed to stammer out, "Er — well . . . I'll go and get my boss."

The boss arrived and I explained the situation; that I was going abroad and selling what furniture, etc., I could.

To cut a long story short, the young man's boss went away one hour later complete with one carpet, one rather old carpet sweeper, one mirror and a few other odds and ends.

So take heart, even the fastest talker can be out-talked. It's easy — and I've got the money to prove it!

Complete Story by BAR JONES

IF ONLY....

H E sat on top of the wooden gate and looked down across the town. The red glow of the wintry sun was filtered and dulled by the smoke. He knew the narrow streets below would already be enveloped in premature dusk.

Up here was the nearest he could get to the pure country air. Up here where once moorlands had stretched unhindered for mile after mile.

Now, the science fiction outline of a power station slashed the sky behind him, and already the ugly Tarmac roads writhed up the valley sides towards it.

"Progress," his friend Jack had said. "No stopping progress, Dave. You want a smokeless zone, you've got to get heat from somewhere. You can't have your cake and eat it, lad. It's either the moors or the smoke, which would you rather have?"

It was unanswerable. Yet the monster at his back depressed him unbearably. It seemed to wear an air of grotesque triumph, and the retreating countryside moved a few miles farther back.

He looked down once more, seeing the dirty huddle of streets that was the old town, and the new estates extending the boundary on the far side of the valley.

Here was his home, as indistinguishable from the others as a matchbox from its fellows. Inside it, in the spotless contemporary kitchen, Kitty, his wife, would be cooking supper.

He could picture her with the ease of 10 years of memories — small and tidy, like the house. Fair haired and blue eyed with a neat figure and well-groomed, sensible clothes. She looked after their children competently, shopped economically, always had his supper ready when he came home from the factory.

Poor Kit, he thought with strange, sad affection. She was everything a modern housewife should be — and unutterably boring.

Suddenly he jumped down from the gate, kicking viciously at a stone on the path. All right, what did he want? He was no young idealist. At 35 he had a good, responsible job, a smart home in the right area, two boys who were, according to his family, "a credit to him." And Kitty.

Again he saw her before him, and tried in vain to remember why he had married her. It was all so long ago. So much had changed in 10 years. Yet had it changed? He tried to remember how he had felt 10 years ago.

Strong enough to change the world? Well, if not the world, at least this small, grimy Welsh town. Then his ideal had been all the things he now rejected.

Above all, he had wanted a wife. Someone of his own whom he could love without reservation.

Two small words that can mean the difference between reality . . . and a dream come true . . .

That someone had been Kitty Davis. Now he thought that it might have been almost anyone. Anyone, like Kitty, who had been willing to conform to his idea of the Perfect Wife.

He had vested her with the qualities she lacked, used the basic material of a nice, quiet girl to build the fictitious vision of his own mind. And he had succeeded.

He laughed shortly as he thought how well he had succeeded.

Kitty, herself, had forgotten her own identity in being Dave's wife, Jim and Peter's mother. Of course, he hadn't known he was doing it, but he had created an ideal unthinking automaton. And now, perversely, he was dissatisfied.

HE began to walk slowly along the footpath to the stile, and almost as he reached it, a black mongrel flung itself over, narrowly missing him.

"Hi!" He was jerked abruptly out of his day-dreams.

"Here, boy," he said, extending his hand. The dog wagged an enormous tail, but stayed where it was. Dave saw the short leather leash dangling from its collar.

"Come on, boy. Come here. Now where have you escaped from?" He squatted down on his heels, talking soothingly to the dog.

Behind him, a girl came breathlessly over the stile.

"Oh, you naughty boy! Come here this minute!"

Dave looked up, smiling. "He seems to have a mind of his own."

"Yes." She laughed. "Not always a good thing!"

He stood up. "I suppose not." The girl had cool, blue eyes, and chestnut hair. His insides did a queer somersault, and he looked away from her and back at the dog. "Is he yours?"

"Yes, well, he's my father's. We live at the farm over there. I've seen you here a lot. Do you live down there?"

"Yes," he said, and made a face. "But not from choice."

"You prefer the country?"

"Yes."

Again there was a silence, and Dave felt the thudding of his heart.

"I'm Ceridwen Hughes," she said, holding out her hand. "And the dog is Shonin." Her eyes sparkled with merriment.

He looked down at the proffered hand. Half-afraid, he took it, and the touch of her fingers was as he had known it would be. Neither spoke, yet a communication was made, and their hands stayed together too long.

"Shonin," he said brightly over the sudden dryness in his throat, "that's John, isn't it?"

"Yes." She had let go his hand, and he felt suddenly forlorn. "Do you speak Welsh, then?"

"No, I'm English. Quite a few English in the town."

"Yes."

"You must come and see the farm," she was saying, "if you like the country so much."

It's now that I should tell her, he thought. I should say, "Yes, I'll come to the farm and bring my wife and kids. They'll love it."

But he couldn't.

"I'd love to come," he said very quietly and left it at that.

Kitty and the burning supper intruded upon the dream. "I must go now, I've been here too long as it is." He almost turned to go, and she said quickly:

"Could you come up on Sunday afternoon?"

He looked down into her eyes and calmly made his decision.

"Yes, I'll come on Sunday."

She laughed. "Do you know, you haven't even told me your name?"

"It's Dave, Dave Connell."

"David," she said with strange intensity, her voice soft with accent. "Well, that's Welsh enough."

THE rest of the week was hell. His conscience tore at him day and night. At the factory he was silent and preoccupied. At home Kitty's eyes over the knitting needles bored into his brain.

The children annoyed him, and the necessary lies he was forced to tell about Sunday tormented him. In the silence of the bedroom he shared with his wife, he lay sleepless into the night.

Often he almost reached the point of telling Kitty about the chance meeting, then forgetting it. But his wife's hunched shoulder in the other bed, the regularity of her breathing, reminded him that she didn't even know he was troubled.

If she had inquired after him once, to care if he was sleepless, he would have unburdened himself gladly. But she did not, and in the darkness he saw only a pair of strange blue eyes and heard a soft voice saying, "David."

On Sunday he raced up the hillside like a schoolboy on his first date. She was waiting for him in a pair of jeans, a checked shirt and a huge, chunky pullover. Her eyes were just as he remembered.

"Hello," he said, "it's a lovely day."

"Hello, David," she said simply, and any vague resolutions he might have had were lost.

Her parents were charming. True old Welsh farmers, with a simplicity of life he envied.

Dave found the tensions of months and years slipping from him. The old couple were courteously cool, showing none of the feigned enthusiasm with which townsfolk greet strangers.

He had a feeling they disapproved slightly of a man of his age taking up with their daughter. If only they knew, he thought briefly. Yet strangely his conscience was quiet.

Was it simply that here he was not Dave Connell, factory worker, father of two, husband of Kitty? He was simply David, and more himself than he had ever been.

Ceridwen's cool eyes never left his face, and his own continually returned to her at any lapse of conversation. The hours passed swiftly, and he was invited to call again. He accepted gladly, pleased that Mr and Mrs Hughes had liked him, and Ceridwen walked with him to the gate.

He did not touch her. He simply said, "Goodnight, Ceridwen."

"Goodnight, David. Thank you for coming." The words were simple, even formal, but the sunset flushed her face with splendour, and, in the gathering dusk, her eyes seemed to shine for him alone.

He didn't look back, but walked swiftly down into his other life. And again, routine closed about him.

The days were now only frustrating gaps between meetings with Ceridwen. Long drawn, meaningless blanks to be got through before he could live.

He noticed Jack's puzzled looks, Kitty's bewilderment, and the inventions got more improbable each time.

He was going fishing — meeting an old friend Kitty didn't know — going to a business lunch. He knew it couldn't last. But he wasn't reasoning clearly, and he didn't care.

His relationship with Ceridwen grew and deepened. He told himself that it was friendship, she understood him, liked what he liked, talked the same language.

Yet he was intensely aware of her physically. And he did not dare to touch her. Not even to hold her hand or help her over a fence when they went walking together. He knew it would be a spark to gunpowder, and he feared the explosion.

On their walks he talked. About his short and happy London childhood, ending when his parents had both been killed and he had come to live with his aunt in Wales.

They had been good to him, but naturally their own sons came first. He always felt a poor second to Ivor and Richard, older and brighter than he.

They had laughed at his early attempts to learn their language, and after a while he had stopped trying. So he remained a small, resentful alien, and much of the boyish small-talk had passed him by.

He'd worked hard and got a good job, met a few English friends and the conflict with his cousins was forgotten years ago.

He had made his place in the town, and supposed that he had been lucky, really. Yet there had been something missing.

All this he told to Ceridwen, only halting at the story of his marriage. It was no conscious effort to halt there — 10 years of his life was blank when he was with her.

She would listen quietly, occasionally asking questions, her eyes on his face as he spoke. In spite of his absorption in his own story, he was always conscious of her.

THE weeks grew to months, and this part of his life became the most real.

Summer came and went and the harvest ripened. Dave found himself working in the little fields beside Mr Hughes and Ceridwen. There was deep satisfaction in the hard work, lifting, carrying, breathing the wonderful wine-air of the moorlands.

One golden evening he and Ceridwen were sitting, their backs to the sheaves, drinking cold lager and eating sandwiches. She seemed to have caught the sun somehow, and imprisoned it in the softness of her skin.

Her bare arms were honey coloured, and her open-necked shirt revealed the warm line of her throat. She lay back against the corn, gold on gold, and smiled at him.

"How would you like to be a farmer, David?"

"I'd like it very much," he said thickly, choked with emotion at the sight of her.

Suddenly, her face changed. The light died, and she sat up abruptly, wrapping her arms about her knees.

"What is she like?" she said softly, staring out over the smoke haze of the town. The words chilled Dave.

"Who?"

"Your wife."

"Ceri!" Unconsciously, he slipped into his secret pet name for her.

"I've guessed for a long time, David, but now I'm sure."

"Why? What — what has made you so sure?" His voice sounded unfamiliar.

"You told me everything, but I felt there was something missing. I knew it, yet I didn't want to believe it. But I'm certain it's true when you look at me like that."

"Like what?"

"I'm not a child, David." Her eyes were sadly accusing, then she looked away again. "I shouldn't say this. I probably have no pride."

He couldn't see her face, the delicate profile silhouetted against the sunset.

"I love you, David."

The world spun before him in glorious undreamed-of colours and visions. In the long silence a blackbird sang with wild delight on the hedgerow.

"Ceri —"

"Don't say anything. Please, don't say you're sorry or anything!"

)d, and walked away from him to the edge of the field.
t slowly to his feet and followed her. Gently, he put his hands
shoulders, feeling her stiffen.
i, I love you, too." At last he had said the words haunting his
.

She kept her back to him, saying brightly, "How many children did
you say you have?"

Stung, he gripped her shoulders. "Ceridwen! Ceri! Please —"

There was such a world of pain in his voice that she turned in his arms.
"David —"

H E looked down at her, the blood pounding in his veins. She repeated
his name softly, and then he was kissing her. Incredibly, it was
their first kiss, and in it love hardened to passion, attraction to
desire.

She jerked away from him, tears bright in her eyes. "Why, David?
Why didn't you tell me?"

"If I had, would you have let me come here?"

She didn't answer for a moment, then said softly, "Could I have
stopped you? I loved you when I first saw you."

"Darling —".

"No! I have no right to such expressions!"

She looked fully into his eyes. "David, if I lie down in this field, I
can't see the power station or the town. I can pretend they don't exist,
that I'm far away in the country.

"But that doesn't alter the facts. The power station is still there, for
all my wishing, and the dirty little houses are just over the hill. I think
you've been lying in a field these last few months."

"I've come alive, Ceri," he said awkwardly, "these months with
you."

"No, not with me. You think you love me right now, but you don't.
You love an ideal. Someone to talk to, to dream with. I'm just different
from your wife, that's all."

"She — she doesn't understand —"

"Oh, please spare me that!" For the first time her voice was angry.
"Don't talk like a cheap novel!"

He turned away from her, his hands covering his face.

"David! Oh, darling, I'm sorry." She touched his arm.

"It's true," he said in a muffled voice. "She doesn't understand me,
but then I don't understand her. I tried to push her into being something
else, and for so long now I've just seen my own problems and not hers."
He took his hands from his face. "But oh, Ceri, I do love you.
You must believe that."

She looked into his eyes, long and deeply. "Yes, David, I do believe
you. But that doesn't alter anything. You're still married, you still
belong down there."

"I belong here."

"No." She shook her head. "You've just played at farming."

There was an edge of bitterness in her voice, and he remembered Jack
once saying acidly, "All this talk of green fields, but I never notice
you planning to live out there."

44

His whole world, his vision of himself, were being destroyed. "Where do I go from here?" he said, half to himself.

"Go? You go right home to your neat little house, to your wife and family, David. And never," her voice broke. "Never come back."

He looked at her in pained wonder. "You say you love me, and yet —"

"That's why, darling, can't you see? It's because I love you. I want the best for you, and me. I want you to remember me with — love. Not with shame because we had a cheap affair. Because you wouldn't divorce your wife, now would you?"

He thought of the details of divorce, the custody of the boys, the loss of all they had built up in 10 years.

"How old are you, Ceridwen?"

"Twenty."

Twenty. He remembered Kitty, breathless in white lace, orange-blossom in her hair. He had changed her from an enthusiastic girl into a conventional wife and mother. Probably she thought it was what he wanted.

"Go home, David," Ceridwen said quietly. "She'll be waiting for you."

He thought of the anxious frown she'd begun to wear whenever he came home from these mysterious outings lately. Poor Kit, she must have been tortured.

Then he looked down at the girl beside him. Her freshness, the smooth skin and the frank blue eyes held him as surely as ever.

"Ceri — I can't —"

"You must. Believe me, David. You know how I feel, I can't say it again." The sob tore at her throat once more, and he reached out for her.

"Don't touch me, please. If you do, I'll never let you go. I'll cling to you and beg you not to leave me. Oh, David, why did you ever come here?"

"I don't know," he said slowly, "I really don't. You didn't mean that about not seeing you again, did you? Surely once in a while would do no harm?"

"Yes, I meant it. Never."

She waved her hand. "This land is up for sale anyway. They want it for factories, so Father decided to get out. There'll be no harvest from this field next year.

"And before you ask, I won't give you my address. Forget this, David, it's been an interlude for you."

"And you?" His voice was tender.

"When you lose a limb, it takes time for it to heal. I suppose when you lose your heart it just takes longer, that's all."

"Oh, Ceridwen —"

"Go, David. Go quickly and don't look back." She was crying. He bent and kissed her wet cheek without passion.

Then he went, striding swiftly across the stubble. Below him the lights of the town were beginning to come on, and somewhere among them, Kitty, his wife, would be waiting.

The End.

... AND IF ONE MILK BOTTLE SHOULD ACCIDENTALLY FALL...

Next time you take your milk from your doorstep, says Patricia Beard, spare a thought for the pale-faced, sleep-starved milkman who made it possible . . .

FOR some strange reason, people like to see their milk on the doorstep by breakfast time. Why, I simply can't imagine! In these days of domestic refrigeration one would suppose any regular delivery time would do. But — oh, no . . . if a milkman doesn't deliver promptly and he hasn't a monopoly, he's likely to lose his customers.

And, believe me, I know. For my husband and I had a country milk round for three years.

Trying to get everyone's milk on their doorstep before noon kept my husband and me on the move all the time. At five every morning we loaded the van with crates of silver, gold and green-topped milk bottles, trays of eggs and cream and yoghurt. Half an hour later we were off.

For the next four hours we ran — up paths and down paths, up lanes and down lanes, tight lipped and perspiring. Never a word did we speak to each other. Whoever got back to the van first drove it on to the next stop.

It was a point of honour with us to finish the last customer by noon. Even then we still had to unload the van, hose it down — dried milk smells — and do our books.

"Doing the books" was a chore at first but our memories soon stretched to incredible proportions.

Because most people had a regular daily order, we had only to remember the actual changes. Mrs Jones who asked for two extra pints, Mrs Smith who cancelled today's and Mrs Brown who had an unexpected dozen eggs.

While we were still referring to the books on the round, I did a terrible thing. I had a whole road to deliver by myself and I gave every house the next neighbour's order.

Mrs Thornton, with a large family to feed, was presented with one solitary pint and old Miss Lane, living alone, was horrified to find six pints, one dozen eggs, ½ lb. butter and a carton of cream on her doorstep.

This sort of thing could never happen once the customers' orders were known. Even then they were frequently just names and houses, not faces. The milkman seldom meets his customers. Some on payday, but those who pay by monthly or weekly cheque, never.

To me, a slow starter, those first few months of rising at four-thirty were sheer purgatory. The only compensation was seeing the dawn.

However, on winter mornings most of our work was carried out in the pitch dark. Next time you leave a note out for your milkman remember that he may have to read it without a light. Juggling with a torch would be just too much — he only has two hands! I wish people who put out their empties once a week and feel aggrieved if they're not removed would remember that.

I've sometimes had cryptic messages or pages and pages of instructions left out for me to read. At times they've been sodden and torn but I'd hardly be popular ringing the doorbell at six a.m. for a translation.

The one section of the public that really make me mad are those who think tradesmen don't merit consideration.

I remember one lady who watched impassively from her front room window while I struggled in the pouring rain with her warped gate, trudged up her path, smiled at her as I passed and walked right around the house to the back as usual. On the step was a note. "No milk today."

She probably thought the exercise would do me good!

Sickness was a constant bogy hanging over us because the round was too big for one.

In three years of slogging on, right through Christmas Day, Easter and Bank Holidays my husband had only one day off. He visited his father who was seriously ill and the distance was

too great for him to return in twelve hours. So I offered to do the round alone.

I took so long that when I had finished I reloaded and started again with the next day's milk. I reasoned that a good sleep at the end was better than a short spell in the middle. But creeping around back doors at two in the morning isn't conducive to good relations with your customers!

It's disconcerting to bend over at the back door and have it open for someone to throw their cat out — especially when they scream with fright at the sight of you. The usual cheery "good morning" doesn't quite meet the case, somehow.

EVENTUALLY we forgot what a social life was like — we hadn't got one! People gave up asking us out because we gained a reputation for falling asleep in the middle of the evening.

It began to dawn on us that we were devoting our lives to placing "pintas" on doorsteps. "Getting the milk out!" had begun to assume the importance of "Getting the good news from Ghent to Aix."

One day an incident occurred which really brought this home to me. At one shop we supplied, I always had to ask the owner how many pints he wanted. On this particular day the poor man had a bad accident just before I arrived.

I elbowed my way past the crowd, only one thought in my mind. I leaned over him, asked my question and got my answer. His last words gasped out before being taken to the hospital were, "Ten pints, please."

It wasn't until I was driving away that the enormity of what I'd done hit me. I was sick with shame.

I knew then that it was time for both of us to go on to pastures new and we sold our milk round. I pity the new people who've taken it over — they looked as enthusiastic as we did when we began. Never mind, good luck to them — "one extra pinta please!"

The End.

IT'S a tough life being an Alsatian, can tell you. All this bally-hoo abou us being the best, the fiercest, the mo intelligent dogs in the canine world pu an awful burden on us, you know.

We're supposed to have film st looks. I blame old, what's-his-name Tin-Tin and-more-Tin or whatever it i for all that malarkey. Every one of u Alsatians has it Rin-Tin-dinned into u how to sit, how to show our best profile how to smile. "Always think of th cameras!" my mother used to say.

Being fierce — that puts a strain o us. We're expected to face anythin from a vicious gunman to a mob c rioters, and keep calm. Huh! Would yc feel particularly calm facing th wrong end of a gun?

As for being the most intelligent c dogs, well, I wouldn't exactly — er — disagree with that. But again, you see it places such a burden, mentall speaking, on us.

I mean to say, where would all yo good people be if the police force didn't have us around? Law and orde depends on us. So my old man once tol me. And the country depends on lav and order being upheld. So he said and I wouldn't call him anything bu truthful, the country depends on us.

I wonder if the Prime Minister and th rest of those politicians realise hov much they owe to us?

I
LIKE
PEOPLE

49

Can you remember those wartime days, when a banana was one of the most priceless treasures anyone could possess . . . ?

I REMEMBER so well that day when Madge brought the banana to school, for it was also the day when Kate arrived.

The two events, now, are inextricably interwoven in my memory, so that when I peel a creamy-skinned banana and sink my teeth into the soft flesh, I think of Kate's black, hopeless eyes as she stood in the classroom facing us all, like a Christian about to be thrown to the lions.

The banana came first.

Madge was obviously excited when I sauntered into the playground that morning. I glanced at her, unmoved.

Madge was a great one for drama. She made the utmost of the trivial. The purchase of a new hair ribbon was described with arm wavings and flashing eyes; an extra large piece of

Complete Story by ANNE GORING

BANANAS

shrapnel found in the street to add to her collection might have been solid gold the way her plump fingers caressed it.

It was no surprise to me when, years later, she started raking in rewards for her stage performances.

She ran through the crush when she saw me. She came like a round butterball — she'd slimmed to an incredible fragility by the time she was appearing in the West End — her cheeks rosy, her auburn hair flying from her shoulders in bunched ringlets.

I envied her her hair. Mine remained stubbornly straight, despite the care my mother took putting it in rag curlers every night.

I was born too soon, of course. My own daughter can wear hers straight and shining and look absolutely stunning. Then, we were in the post-Shirley Temple era and curls and dimples were valuable assets.

She cried, "You'll never guess what, Tessa!"

"Your rabbit had its babies."

"No, think again."

"Mmm. You heard from your American pen-friend."

"No, no. It's important."

"Oh! You got your uniform. You lucky . . ."

"*Important*," she said, her eyes dancing. She loved this game.

I began to take notice. Since we'd passed the scholarship for high school, the prospect of getting our smart green uniforms had been gloated over daily. For it to be dismissed so lightly was surprising.

She saw my interest.

"P'raps I'll leave it until later. Tell you when we're in class," she promised.

"Beast," I said, without heat.

"Well," she said, "I'll tell you part of it."

I gave an exaggerated yawn. "Did you get up for the raid last night? It's ages since we had one. We just went under the stairs and I went to sleep, so Mum left me there . . ."

"My dad came home on leave yesterday!" She hopped from one foot to the other, rewarded by the sight of my widened eyes.

"Honest?" I breathed.

"Honest," she said. "He's ever so brown, so he's been somewhere hot, but he can't say where and he looks smashing in his uniform and he brought us . . ."

The bell interrupted this flow of information. We marched in our lines across the now silent playground and into school. We hurried to our classroom, anxious to make the most of the few minutes before Miss Faith arrived. We sat at our double desk and Madge lifted the lid to screen us from the others.

One plump hand dived into her gas-mask case, where she usually kept her lunch biscuits.

"Crikey," I said. "A banana."

SHE laid it carefully on the box that held her books and pencils in the desk. We stared down at it in silence.

It was not, I think, a particularly attractive banana. It was small and its yellow peel was heavily and darkly spotted. The skin at one end was torn and the flesh beneath discoloured.

"I can just remember," I said

EVERY DAY

faintly, "what a banana tastes like." My mouth watered at the thought.

"You can't possibly remember *tastes*," Madge scoffed.

"You can," I said stubbornly. "I can anyway."

"Before the war," Madge said, boasting, "we used to have bananas every day. I liked them mashed up with sugar and cream."

Madge sighed. It wasn't her acting kind of sigh. It was small. Little more than a slow exhalation of breath.

We looked at each other, solemnly aware, perhaps for the first time, that this world we considered normal, this world of blackouts and air raids and dig-for-victory and marge-instead-of-butter and windows criss-crossed with sticky tape against bomb blast, was merely an interruption and would one day be gone.

"You can have half," said Madge. "We'll have half each at playtime."

IF I HAD MY WAY

I'D have one of these toys in every room! They're marvellous. You pick up a bit of it and a squeaky voice says, "Number, please? Hello? Hello . . . ? Hello! HELLO!"

It's better and more reliable than the talking doll that silly sister of mine has!

If you keep this toy in your hand, the voice goes on talking to you. It says, "Why don't you go and fetch Mummy?" and other things like, "Put that phone down!"

And when you do, and then pick it up again, the voice starts all over again — "Number, please? Hello? Hello . . . ? Hello! HELLO!"

Of course I know this is one of those special toys for grown-ups. My mum just loves it. She talks to it for hours. Really she does!

"And how are you?" she coos into it. "I'm fine. Oh, I must tell you what happened to me this morning . . ."

As if a toy cared what happened to her!

I'm not very keen on this "toys-for-grown-ups" stuff and "baby-keep-off" stuff.

I'm a great believer in sharing things around. My old man keeps taking a sip out of my bottle of orange juice . . . but I never get offered a sip out of the bottle he drinks!

This toy has a bell on it somewhere. I wish I could find where. I'd smash it quick. Every time it tinkles, Mum comes through, looks at me, and snatches me up. "Not again!" she cries. "Oh, you naughty thing, you!"

I wish I could find that noisy, interfering bell.

THOUGHT FOR TODAY
Think of a number. But don't hope to get it — if it's ours!

"Put down your desk lid, Madge." Miss Faith flicked her cool glance round the classroom. We sat up very straight and folded our arms.

Madge nudged me and hissed between unmoving lips, a technique she had perfected after reading "How To Become A Ventriloquist" in a comic: "Look what the cat dragged in."

THE child standing quite still by Miss Faith was a little scarecrow. We were all used to make-do-and-mend. But our mothers took pride in keeping us tidy despite ration books and coupons.

This child wore an assortment of ill-fitting garments. An unevenly-hemmed skirt that hung from her thin shoulders by unmatching straps and gaped at the waist. A blouse that was meant to be short-sleeved but which fell in limp folds below her elbows. Scuffed sandals and socks that were not a pair completed her outfit.

53

Above all this a pair of black sad monkey eyes peered from a pale, pointed face.

"This is Kate," Miss Faith said briskly. "She comes from London and is going to be with us for the rest of the term. Now I want her to sit with someone sensible who will look after her."

Her eyes moved round the room then came to rest on me. "Madge, dear, if you will move behind with John, Kate can sit next to Tessa."

Madge gave a ventriloquial groan. "Keep an eye on the banana."

"It would be today," I muttered.

I had not practised so well as Madge.

"No chatting, Tessa," Miss Faith said, frowning. She added pointedly, "And I trust both you and Madge to see that Kate is made to feel welcome." She gave the girl a gentle push in my direction.

I tried a smile but it was not a success. She glowered back at me, sensing, no doubt, the chilliness of the reception.

From behind, Madge whispered, "Tell her she's not to start poking around in my desk."

Kate swivelled her head on her thin white neck.

"I don't want nuffin' to do with your daft ol' desk," she said sharply.

"Good heavens," Madge said, "it speaks. But whatever language is it?"

Her rolling Cockney fell oddly on our northern ears. I giggled.

"I speak English," Kate said, "Same as everybody else normal. Not the stuff you talk 'ere."

"Now that you've made friends," Miss Faith called, "we'll have no more talking. And, children, we shall be having an air-raid drill sometime this morning. Make sure you take your gas masks."

I chanced a quick glance at Madge; she rolled her eyes in despair. It seemed that fate was well and truly against us today. If we went off to air-raid drill before playtime it meant leaving the banana alone and unguarded in the classroom.

L OOKING back, it seems ridiculous that we could create such melodrama around one not-too-appetising fruit. But children are odd creatures of mood and sudden violent enthusiasms.

When the air-raid bell shrilled we gathered our gas masks and went in orderly lines along the dark brown tiled corridors. Madge and I and an unwilling Kate, whom I clutched by the arm in a not-too-kind grip, contrived to be near the end.

"I don't wan' to go down," she said, stopping suddenly so that the kids behind concertinaed into us.

"Don't be silly," I said crossly. "We've got to go." I pulled her arm. She shuffled her feet.

"It's daft," she said. "Practisin' for air raids when there isn't one."

I was exasperated with this silly, gipsyish child.

"All we do is sit on the stairs and try on our gas masks. Then we come back to our classrooms. It doesn't take long."

Madge caught her other arm. Between us we hustled her down the rest of the way. We sat on the steps squashed together.

Miss Faith picked her way up the stairs.

"Gas masks on, children," she said.

We stuck our faces chin first into the rubbery-smelling masks. Immediately the face-pieces misted over and we laughed at each other and peered through the fog that our breath had caused. Some of the boys made satisfactorily rude noises through theirs.

Kate had made no attempt to get her mask out of its case.

"Hurry up," I said, my voice sounding funny and gruff.

She shook her head fiercely at me, her mousy locks flicking about her bony forehead.

Miss Faith was moving up towards us and, much as I was irritated by this strange child, I felt I had to give her some protection. I groped about for her case.

She snatched it out of my hand. "Stop it," she said, her voice rising.

Madge said, sounding equally unreal, "Don't be such a baby."

Then I noticed that Kate was scared. Her face was green, her eyes enormous and wild. I thought: We must frighten her. It must be the gas masks.

"It's only a practice," I said, not understanding.

L IKE a full stop to my sentence, somewhere a door crashed shut. In the same instant, Kate half rose in panic. Then her mouth opened.

I winced, waiting for the scream to meet my eardrums. But she didn't make a sound. Just crouched there, like a ragged monkey, a white face among all the grotesque rubber ones, with her mouth gaping in a soundless scream.

I pulled off my gas mask to reason with her. The cool air hit my hot, damp cheeks.

I put out my hand to Kate, but she was no longer there. Like a hurdler, she was off up the steps, leaping over legs and shoulders, racing to the brown gloom of the corridor back to the classroom.

Miss Faith saw her. In long strides she followed. I looked at Madge across the gap where Kate had been.

"Crumbs," Madge said. "What a chump. Miss Faith will be furious."

CLIFF HANGER

At one of our Guild meetings the subject was — "My Most Exciting Adventure." Every member had a turn at describing theirs, each one more thrilling than the last.

Then came the turn of a very shy, elderly lady. She was rather diffident about beginning, but when she did she began describing an adventure in which she'd climbed down a steep cliff in search of gulls' eggs.

As she slowly described every move, we were all enthralled, and could hear the waves crashing at the foot of the cliff.

When she told us how she'd slipped and grasped at a bush that came out at the roots we were almost hysterical. Someone shrieked . . . "And what happened then?"

"I landed with a thump on the bedside rug!" She chuckled.

Good for Gran!

Though we didn't say it, we knew we should be in for it, too.

We were no sooner back in the classroom than the bell went for playtime. We jumped up.

"Stay behind, Tessa and Madge," Miss Faith said. "I want to have a word with you."

There was no sign of Kate. I wondered if she had already been sent for punishment. I thought of her alone and defiant before the Head and tried to believe that it would serve her right.

But I could only remember that dreadful, soundless scream. And somehow it seemed all our fault. Perhaps if Madge and I had been more pleasant and not so concerned with the banana . . .

It was still there, lying in the desk, and I hated it.

"I'm telling you this," Miss Faith began, "because I want you to understand."

The empty room seemed to catch her words and send them winging back from the picture-strewn walls to the chalk-smeared blackboard.

"You see, Kate has been through rather a difficult time."

I jerked back, surprised. Miss Faith was not cross. She seemed sad.

"Both she and her family were buried under their house in one of the raids on London. Her mother and her young sisters are still recovering in hospital. Her father is a prisoner of war in Germany. She's staying with an aunt here and, if her appearance is a little odd, well, the family lost all their possessions when they were bombed.

"That's why she was so frightened this morning — and why I want you to be particularly kind to her."

For some reason I thought of my own father as he came home each night tired and dirty and greasy from the engineering factory where he worked. And my mother tucking my brother into bed and giving me a hug before I left for school.

I tried to imagine myself under the caved-in walls of our house. Waiting, waiting under bricks and rubble. Waiting for someone to come and dig me out.

What had Madge called Kate? A baby. I bit my lip.

"Go and find her," Miss Faith said. "Look after her. She'll be in the playground."

WE found her propping up the wall near the girls' entrance. She was alone, as though her imprudent behaviour had cut her off from the others.

She curled her lip up when she saw us. Her eyes were dark and defiant.

"Wotcher want?" she asked ungraciously.

"Such manners," Madge said in conscious imitation of Miss Faith, "when all we want to do is be friendly."

"Humph," Kate said, folding her arms across her skimpy chest. "Don't need no friends."

Madge and I hesitated. We looked at each other as if in agreement.

Slowly Madge drew her hand from behind her back.

"Know what this is?"

Kate viewed the object without interest. "It's a banana."

Madge nodded. She took a deep breath and said, "It's for you as a present just to show you we really want to be friends and we're sorry

56

Continued on page 58

WE LIKE PEOPLE

ESPECIALLY people who let us out of our cage. Do you blame us?

How would YOU like to be cooped up day in, day out, in a small wire bin?

We also like poeple who talk. We talk ourselves, you know. And that's more than you can say about all the cats, dogs and what-have-you pets you care to name!

But even though we can have a chat with you now and again, life isn't exactly rosy for us.

We spend so much time preening ourselves in the mirror, buffing our beaks till they shine and practising the most flirtatious attitudes — and for what?

For someone to poke at us with their finger and cluck, "Kiss for Joey!"

It's insulting, that's what it is!

And does anybody ever teach us the latest top twenty hit? Oh, no! Silly little nursery jingles — that's all we get.

Ah well, we mustn't grumble too much — or someone will throw a dark cloth over our cage to keep us quiet. But at least we'd have some privacy . . .

Mind you, it's not a bad life. We are pampered really. Plenty to eat, lots to drink, a well-furnished cage, and allowed out now and again for a flutter.

You can't have everything, can you?

your mum's in hospital and everything," she finished in a rush.

She thrust the banana into Kate's hands. We both stood back.

It lay in Kate's palm. Her fingers closed over it and for a horrible moment I thought she was going to toss the gift back at us.

But she just said, less defiantly, "Is this what your secret was?"

We nodded.

"And it's for me?"

We nodded again, feeling the warmth of self-sacrifice.

"Ta," she said shortly. Her deft fingers peeled down the skin, her sharp teeth bit once into the flesh. Then her long lashes lifted and there was something like mischief lurking in the depths of her eyes.

With great dignity she broke what was left of the banana into three equal pieces. We accepted our share solemnly. We ate. We ran the last delicious melting crumbs round our tongues. We sighed with satisfaction.

In the manner of little girls then and now, we proceeded to twine our arms around each other. Locked together, the three of us shoved our way between the clusters of playing, uncaring children.

Madge, as always, took the initiative.

"Of course . . ." she began, as Kate and I turned our faces towards her ". . . of course, when the war's over, I shall have bananas *every* day . . ."

The End.

Not Wealthy . . . But Rich!

EVERY Saturday afternoon her chauffeur takes her for a drive. Every Wednesday afternoon her gardener tidies up her garden. Every morning, just after nine o'clock, her "help" is there to see what chores and errands need to be done.

No, she's not a wealthy old lady. In fact, she lives on her old-age pension and little else.

But it's true she's rich. Rich in good neighbours.

Her "chauffeur" is the schoolteacher who lives two streets away and never forgets that old ladies love to see the countryside.

Her "gardener" is the local butcher, who cheerfully spends part of his half day to keep her garden ablaze with colour.

Her morning "help" is a different woman every day — neighbours who take their turn to give her company and assistance.

I don't know who started it all. But it's a very wonderful thing. And the longer it goes on the more people want to help.

A nearby neighbour offered to come and clean her windows. Someone else wanted to paint her kitchen.

She refused their offers as nicely as she could.

"There are so many like me," she told them. "I have so much already — please find someone else and give them what I have."

She's right. There are so many like her who do need help, who yearn for company, who would dearly love to be taken out now and again.

Look around you — perhaps there is someone *you* could help right now. Think about it.

"MY MUM SAYS WE'VE GOT SKELETONS IN OUR CUPBOARD!"

...he cat out of the bag yourself, says MARY BECK. If you don't, ...e children will — and by that time ...he cat will have had kittens . . .

DOUBTLESS everybody has his secret. For all I know Aunt Mabel hides brandy in the wardrobe, and Mrs Smith over the road plays roulette in the front room. But whatever they do, they keep their vices strictly to themselves.

Now I'm all for this. Live and let live, is my motto. An Englishman's home is his castle, and all the rest of it!

The trouble is, my own particular castle has been rendered defenceless of late — drawbridge down and not a pot of boiling oil in sight.

From the moment my eldest daughter opened her mouth and said, "Do you know what my mummy does?" every skeleton in the family cupboard has been dragged, rattling, into the light of day.

Alas for privacy! Alas for those carefree, bygone days when I could indulge in nasty little habits.

Little habits like dusting off the Sunday joint after accidentally dropping it on the floor, effecting last-minute repairs with a safety-pin, putting the salt packet on the table when pushed for time . . .

I still do, of course, but with a horrid sensation that the whole shameful incident will be noised throughout the neighbourhood before sundown.

And noised with great exaggeration into the bargain.

"My mummy never darns Daddy's socks," I heard my daughter remark. "She throws them in the dustbin when they've got holes.

"We never have cakes in our house." She sighed, gazing at a wilting swiss roll in the shop window as if she lived on a constant diet of pease-pudding and gruel.

One evening we dared to have a couple of friends visit us for a quiet drink by the fire at the end of a long,

59

hard day. What happened then?

"Let's have a tea-party," shouted a voice to the heavens the next morning. "I'll bring a bottle of gin."

By now the majority of the neighbours realise that not only do I neglect my husband and starve my children, I'm also a slattern with a tendency to drink.

And that's not all. According to my young daughter, I tell lies as well.

"Sorry about supper," I say brightly to my husband, dishing up sausages and mash without a qualm. "The shops were murder this afternoon. It took me hours to get the groceries."

"Mummy," that innocent little voice says, "tried on lots and lots of shoes, then we had lemonade in the cafe, then we met Auntie Anne and talked and talked and . . ."

There is the heart-stopping business of "having friends to tea." Obviously nobody in their right minds would serve up bread and jam and potato crisps on the kitchen plates, so I make an all-out effort.

Thin sandwiches, the best china, a couple of doyleys about the place for good measure.

"Mummy," my daughter asks in the course of the meal, "why have you put a cloth on the table today?"

All this honesty certainly keeps me on my toes. No more turning socks inside out to last another day, unless I want the manoeuvre proudly explained to anyone who cares to listen.

No more skipping the evening bath, unless I want it generally recognised I never wash my family.

And another thing — my feet are unshakably set on the straight and narrow.

Indeed, after one fearful afternoon when I stupidly offered the plumber a cup of tea and my daughter immediately dashed outside to tell the world I was entertaining a man, I have scarcely dared to smile at the milkman.

OF course, there are compensations, and surely the most wonderful one of all is to discover that other women's children have the same painful leaning towards honesty.

That charming woman living a few doors along, for example. She is always so placid, so sweet tempered. Never a slap or a cross word in that household, I was sure.

"If you don't be quiet this moment," her small boy shouted in a game of mothers and fathers, "I'll come upstairs and give you the hiding of your life."

Oh, joy! Oh, bliss! I know she's human.

The gentleman across the way is another instance. How on earth, I wondered, can his wife manage to turn him out looking like a cross between a tailor's dummy and a suave film star.

"Don't worry about the egg on your shirt, dear," his daughter said in the same revealing game of mothers and fathers. "Just put on your waistcoat and nobody will notice a thing."

Finally, of course, there is my awesome friend.

She is a remarkable woman. Her house is perfect, her kitchen a picture from a glossy magazine, with not even a dirty glass in the sink to mar all that splendour.

I might have gone on regarding her as something superhuman if her young son had not happened to spend an afternoon in the midst of my squalor.

"Quick, quick," he said, hearing the bell ring. "There's somebody at the door. Let's put all the dirty dishes in the oven."

Well, well — interesting creatures, other women's children . . . ☐

I LIKE PEOPLE

MEN who like to talk about motor cars (daft things!) talk in hushed whispers about a Rolls-Royce or a Bentley. And even, thanks to James Bond, about Aston Martins.

Well, please don't think I'm immodest, but we Siamese are the proverbial cat's whiskers in the cat world.

We're expensive to buy. But isn't the best always expensive? We're aloof, so people say, rarely show affection, and can be stubbornly independent. And extremely snooty.

Don't you believe it! Let me tell you the truth. It's all an act. A great big phoney act!

Beneath our sleek, glossy, sable coats we're soft, friendly creatures. Really we are!

If we like you, you're our friend for life. You can even eat some of our fish! But we don't seem to meet many people we like. Is that our fault?

OCCUPATIONAL HAZARDS

No other Siamese for miles.

MOTTO

'CosSiam the best!

THE FIRST STEP

**Complete Story by
EILEEN WILLIAMS**

A RE you out of your min
Maisie?" John Hamilton
eyes were flashing angrily!

"No, John, I'm not. We have
trust Robbie. After all, he's seve
teen. If we don't trust him now, v
never will."

"This is different," John cut
searingly. "Judy Nolan isn't exac
what we've been used to. Don't y
realise what a name she'd made f
herself, and she's only sixteen!"

"Maybe — but we know Robb
don't we?"

John ran a hand through his ha

"Maisie, I'm willing to trust Robb
with anything. But this is the first tin

s ever been serious about a girl and
en that girl happens to be Judy
lan . . . !"

He looked up the stairs to the closed
or of Robbie's room.

I'm going up there to break it up."

John, stop!" I put my hand on his
. "Robbie isn't in love with her.
's only helping her swot for a maths
m. Nothing more."

"Maths exam!" he echoed
iously. With a growl he subsided
a chair and began stuffing tobacco
o his pipe.

ohn and I have been married for
nty-odd years. We'd had our
rrels before, but this was the
t time I'd really stood my ground.
"You're too soft, Mum," Helen,
married daughter, used to tell me.
d I was soft. But not this time.

went through to make a cup of
fee, wondering why I was
ending Judy so strongly.

". . . a disgrace to the parish that
ly Nolan is . . ."

Mrs Smithers at the Mothers'
ion had said that. She had given a
reasons, too, and I felt myself
ckle all over as I remembered.
Then, Robbie had brought Judy
e.

"This is Judy Nolan, Mum," he had
d when he introduced me to the
. "She has a maths exam in a few
eks. I said I'd help her.

"My books are in my room," he'd
ne on. "You don't mind if we go up
re, do you?"

remembered thinking: And what
es Judy Nolan want with maths?
t as I looked into Robbie's clear
e eyes I saw only a boy asking his
ther a perfectly reasonable request.

looked at Judy — at her long, lank
r, framing an appealing face; the
brown eyes and full, smiling mouth.
There was a hint of sadness about
; the way she defiantly wore her

tight jeans; her baggy jersey so out of
place on such a small neat frame.

"Well, it's your room," was all I
said and Robbie had nodded. I could
have sworn he was thinking: It's all
right, Mum, honestly . . .

THE percolator boiled over and I
picked it up.

What was it about Judy that
made me stick up for her? Was it pity?
I knew she didn't have much of a
home. Her mother was a widow and,
from the stories I had heard, never
gave up looking for another
husband . . .

I went to the bottom of the stairs.

"Robbie, I've made coffee for you.
Come and get it!"

John looked up as I went into the
living-room with the tray. I glanced
away.

"Taking their time, aren't they?"
he said impatiently.

Then thankfully the door opened
and Robbie showed Judy in.

"Sorry we were so long, Mum. We
were halfway through an equation
when you called."

Judy's hair was neatly combed and
the ink smudges on her fingers made
one feel more than ever that I was
right. We could trust Robbie. We had
to!

Judy seemed afraid of John at first,
but as she drank her coffee the tension
seemed to ease. She showed genuine
enthusiasm over the design on the
cups.

"These are really terrific!" Then
blinking, as though unsure of herself,
she rushed on. "You mustn't mind me
staring at them, Rob's Mum, but
we've nothing like this at Calder
Terrace."

I had to go into the kitchen for
more biscuits. When I went back
Robbie was saying something about
"X" being equal to "B" and Judy

Continued on page 65

MAYBE you have a golden Cocker spaniel already? You do? You don't — oh, that's good. 'Cos I'm looking for someone like you. I don't ask much, you know.

A nice home (central heating preferred to small coal fires), thick, comfortable rugs, draughtproof rooms and deep armchairs complete with cosy cushions.

Add a good supply of food, a fair-sized garden . . .

Am I being unreasonable?

So why don't more people keep a good-looking, highly-intelligent, easily-trained, irresistible (we golden Cockers are very, very modest about ourselves) dog like me?

All good things have a drawback somewhere. I suppose you could say I'm expensive. You could say it — I won't. Since we're the best we come pretty cheap.

That's what I say, anyway! So go on — treat yourself to a dog like me.

Matter of fact, treat yourself to me! I'm just waiting for someone like you . . .

I LIKE PEOPLE

was looking very thoughtful as she listened to what he was saying.

In a quiet fatherly tone John explained something about the value of "Z."

"Maisie," John said when we were alone. "I just don't know what to think. That girl seems as innocent as a babe, yet . . . Well, look at her! Good heavens, I don't know who's kidding who!"

We heard the front door open and a minute later John went up to speak to Robbie.

My heart was thumping as I waited. Now and again I heard John's deep voice and Robbie's, younger sounding — yet calm.

"I know what some people think," I heard Robbie say. "But she's not bad. To me she just seems a bit — well — lost."

I T was several weeks before I saw Judy again. Robbie didn't bring her to the house and, knowing how his father felt, he was wary, more nervous, especially when her name cropped up.

There was one night when John and I came in from the bridge club, I had the feeling Judy had been in. As if to prove my suspicions, Robbie was happier than I'd seen him for a long time.

I couldn't help being curious about Judy now that I was sure Robbie was in love with her and I went to look at her home — Calder Terrace.

It was a back street. The drab, dull brick fronts facing each other; windows, streaked or broken, not hiding torn, unkempt curtains.

What kind of life could she have led here? What chance had she had to have fun like other girls of her age?

I longed to do something about it all, but Robbie avoided the subject.

Then at the Mothers' Union Mrs Ponsonby said pointedly, "Judy Nolan — I'd soon put her in her place if she ran after one of my boys."

I stunned the entire gathering, and myself, by sticking up for Judy as if she were my own daughter. I left them open mouthed and I was so disgusted that I haven't been back since.

I had been looking forward at that time to my birthday. I always do, as it has become a traditional gathering.

Helen arrives with her husband Ralph and Debbie, my only grand-daughter. She's two and I spoil her unmercifully.

Matt, my other son, who's at university, comes too — usually with his latest girlfriend.

And it was Matt who gave me the idea.

He had phoned to tell me they were coming and he laughingly asked if Robbie had anyone in mind . . .

I found Robbie sorting his records.

"Matt's bringing Ursula with him on Saturday," I said lightly. "Would you like to bring somebody?"

He was silent.

"I haven't a special friend," he said at last. "But yes — there is someone I'd like to ask."

"Good."

"No." He shook his head. "Dad wouldn't have it. Judy Nolan."

"I'd like her to come, Robbie. You like her a lot, don't you?"

I expected him to blush, to show his boyishness in a stammer. Instead he looked up at me quite calmly and said, "Yes . . ."

E

I told John over tea later that same night and he shook his head.

"I hope you know what you're doing, Maisie. You could make the girl feel — awkward, you know?"

I was surprised that was all John had to say about it. I was even more surprised he'd actually considered Judy's feelings.

R OBBIE'S face was pale as he introduced Judy to the family. She was wearing a very tight, very short, dress in jade green.

I looked at her and suddenly Robbie's phrase came into my mind: *To me she just seems a bit – well, lost.*

The bewitching mouth was emphasised with a very bright lipstick but, beneath the mascara, her eyes were childish — almost frightened.

But as the afternoon went by it was her long thin arms and hands that fascinated me. They crossed and uncrossed nervously — the hands rising to pat her hair, toying lingeringly around her pale cheeks and scarlet mouth.

When she spoke, she used them almost in mime to illustrate what she was saying.

And then, when the talk shifted, she seemed to relax slightly. Her large brown eyes held a gentleness which, in Calder Terrace, would have been completely out of place.

But it was little Debbie who really sparked Judy into life. She had just wakened from a sleep and was a bit grumpy. Judy asked Helen if she could lift her.

In a moment, the sulky look had gone and Debbie was giggling and chuckling in Judy's arms.

"Ups — a daisy! Ups — a daisy! Ups — a — Debbie!"

Then Judy was down on the floor giving Debbie rides on her back.

"Gee up, Auntie Judy! Gee up — Gee up!" There was a frightening squeal, a bump, then tears.

Helen snatched her up. "There, there, pet. Let me look." But Debbie continued to shriek until her voice subsided to a whimper.

"I want Auntie Judy — I want Auntie Judy . . ."

"Please let me hold her." It was Judy, her arms outstretched.

Helen handed Debbie to her and all was peace once more.

A FTER the success the party had been, Judy came back once or twice to the house with Robbie. And then I heard that they'd had a row and weren't seeing each other at all.

I should really have been pleased because John still wasn't convinced about the girl and with his disapproval never far off Robbie had been becoming tense and bad tempered.

He never told me why they had quarrelled and we never asked. He had proved his trust once and both John and I were sure he knew what he was doing.

Then the police arrived.

At first, I thought something had happened to John. It was a Saturday and he had gone earlier to watch a football match.

"Mrs Hamilton?"

I nodded and said, "Yes," dreading what he was going to say.

"We would like to speak to Robert Hamilton. Your son?"

"Yes. But why — what has he done?"

"We're making enquiries into the disappearance of Miss Judith Nolan. We were told your son was friendly with her."

"Judy — missing? But Robbie went to his sister's for the weekend. Oh — you don't think . . ."

"That they've eloped? That's what we're trying to find out. Mrs Nolan reported her daughter missing this morning. We can't do anything about it, of course, unless a crime is committed. But we must try to find out where the missing person has gone. That's all we want to know just now.

We rang Helen four times in the next half-hour but each time the ringing went unanswered.

With shaking hands I gave them Helen's address, only dimly hearing the policeman ask if we'd had any trouble with Robbie in the past.

"No, none at all," I said.

When they had gone, I sat down, a numb feeling of helplessness washing over me.

"Who Puts The Polar Bears To Bed, Daddy?"

IT was clearly his first visit to a circus, and he sat, quiet and solemn, in a row in front of me with his parents. Not yet four years old, he sensed this was a momentous occasion.

He wasn't quite sure what a circus was about. But he knew he had been brought to it as a special treat.

"I've been a good boy *all* day, haven't I, Mummy?"

One of the first items on the programme was the display of polar bears. As the big animals went through their tricks, the little boy stared at them.

Then the questions started . . .

"Why are there bars? Why can't we go in and pet the nice bears? Why would a polar bear want to be fierce with boys and girls?"

Long after the bears were back in their own cages, and the circus artistes were most successfully entertaining the rest of the audience, one little boy's thought were on "the poor polar bears" which were kept shut up behind bars.

Like a few of the people sitting beside them, his parents were becoming a little exasperated at the loud, piping voice that went on and on and on.

Crisis reared its ugly head with his question of, "Who puts the polar bears to bed, Daddy?" and the irate father's retort of, "I don't know and I don't care! Now watch the circus!"

The tears began . . . and eventually one small boy was hustled away by parents clearly baffled as to why their child couldn't sit and enjoy the show like hundreds of other little boys and girls.

Polar bears . . . railway engines . . . double-decker buses . . . the list of questions a small child can ask about such subjects is endless.

If only we grown-ups could supply the endless answers — or the one answer that would end the questions!

I wonder who does put the polar bears to bed? And to anticipate the next question: What time do they go to bed?

I forced myself to concentrate hard, to think of some clue. Anything.

Had they gone off together and, if so, where? Where would they get the money? Money!

Suddenly I remembered Robbie's building society account book. He kept it in a drawer upstairs. If it was there, it was all right — if it was gone . . . ?

I rushed upstairs and yanked the drawer open. Apart from some neatly-folded shirts, the drawer was empty.

AFTER what seemed hours, I heard the gravel crunching on the path.

I flew downstairs and threw open the door. A policeman stood with hand poised to knock.

"Mrs Hamilton?"

"Yes. Yes. What is it?"

"Your son's all right. We got through to him at your daughter's."

"And Judy? Is she all right, too?" Suddenly I was as concerned over her as I had been about Robbie.

"We're still making enquiries about her, ma'am. That's all I know officially, but I think it'll be all right . . ."

He broke off as John came hurrying up the path.

"Maisie, what on earth's going on? One of the neighbours just told me there's been police at the door all afternoon. What's wrong?"

Within the next five minutes we were both on the telephone again to Helen and this time Helen answered it.

"Stop worrying, Mum," she said. "Judy had an appointment with a Nursery Training School in London this morning. She called here with Robbie before he saw her on the overnight train.

"She actually sounded very keen about it. It seems she's been having a bad time at home and wanted to make a fresh start."

I didn't mention the missing building society book to Helen but I told John. When Robbie came home that night John wanted to see it.

His eyebrows rose in surprise when he saw the amount withdrawn.

"What else could I do, Dad?" Robbie muttered. "She had to get the money somewhere. I was the logical choice."

John smiled. "You really think she's worth it, don't you, Robbie?"

"Yes, Dad."

There was something in the way he answered his father that made me take Robbie's two hands in mine.

"Tell me, Robbie. Are you in love with her?"

"I don't really know." He was thoughtful for a minute. "No, I can't be. I wouldn't have helped her to go so far away, would I? But I do think she'll make good."

Two weeks later, a dozen daffodils were delivered to the door. On the card were three words:

Thanks, Rob's Mum.

A letter followed the next day:

I want to thank you for everything. I'll never forget your birthday. Until then I hadn't known what I wanted from life. Then it came to me that when I'm older I want to be like you. This is my first step . . .

The End.

A WEEKEND AT
MUMPTON GREEN

**It was the last place on earth for any
city girl to go . . .**

IT was at a wedding reception that I let myself in for
it. My cousin Jane was there, with her husband,
Bill. Hordes of friends and relations were milling
around me, in a flurry of flowered silk, white hats and
cigar smoke.

Above the clink of glasses I heard Bill boom at me,
"You ought to come down . . . you've been promising
for months." He turned to his wife.

"Oughtn't she, dear? Oughtn't she to come down to
us for the week-end? Must show her my garden . . ."

"Yes, of course," Jane said warmly. "When can you
come?"

That's when I weakly gave in. "Oh — er — next
week-end?" I said, and led her husband off to the
sandwiches.

So there I was, stuck with the prospect of two whole
days and nights in the back-woods.

Saturday morning found me waiting for a bus to the
station. It was raining, or course!

Saturday noon found me stepping out of the rain on to
a small, almost deserted station. A large poster
confronted me, showing a girl in a yellow swimsuit
holding a red beach ball. The words underneath read:
COME TO MUMPTON-ON-THE-WOLD FOR
YOUR SUMMER HOLIDAY. And somebody had
given the lady a pencilled moustache, adding: *Bring
your macs and umbrellas.*

Outside the station a boy told me that the bus to
Mumpton Green had just gone, and the next one would
be in an hour's time. The station taxi was over at the
church for a wedding, and the trains didn't run to the
Green.

69

I had trudged a full mile along the hot, dusty road, with my mind on how much I could borrow from Dad towards a new pair of shoes, when I heard a car coming up behind me. It slowed down as it drew near, and a voice called, "Want a lift?"

The driver had a wrinkled face and a pink, bald head, and I decided that he would present no problems.

We rattled along the country lanes amidst clouds of dust. Every few yards startled chickens scuttled into the hedgerows, and once a startled boy wheeling a flat-tyred bike scuttled with them. I was just dozing off when we pulled up with a jerk.

"'Ere y'are," he declared. "Mumpton Green. And your friend's house is that one on the corner."

I thanked him, hating to see him go. Now I was well and truly cut off.

Nobody answered my knock, so I ventured round the back of the house. At the end of a very long garden I saw Jane on her knees, grovelling in the earth. She looked round at the click of the garden gate.

"Hello," she called gaily. "Come up here."

I wobbled up the stony path, completing the ruin of my high heels.

"You've come just at the right time." Jane smiled. "I need help with this bit of weeding."

Then, eyeing my new dress rather doubtfully, she added, "Perhaps you'd better not, though. Sit on that old bath over there while I finish . . ."

SO I sat on a rusty, upturned bath, wondering why I had ever agreed to come in the first place.

And then I said it.

"I'm terribly sorry, Jane," I blurted, "but I can only stay for tonight. I'd clean forgotten I promised Maisie Carter I'd go to a special dinner-dance with her — and her brother. It's quite a big affair," I added, carried away by the excitement of finding a way out. "Terribly expensive tickets — and I've got a new dress specially for it."

Jane took it quite calmly. It was a pity I couldn't stay, she said, but there it was, wasn't it? And there I was — with freedom in sight!

I felt so much better that I offered to help get the tea, after which I was detailed to help wash up.

"You shouldn't really," Jane said, pushing a tea towel into my hands.

I even listened to her younger son's recital of "Hiawatha," helped the older one with his homework, listened dutifully to lengthy classical records which Jane adores, and longed for bed-time, when I could shut myself in and read the new novel I'd brought with me. Actually, I managed half a chapter before dozing off.

An unfamiliar clock clanged twice somewhere in the house, and I sat up in bed with a jerk. An owl hooted eerily somewhere in the dark outside, and then came a scrabble from the wainscot — *mice*!

I wondered whether I should climb over my bed and sit out on the window-sill should one dare to come out into the open.

I spent the remainder of the night staring about me, with my shoe in my hand, ready to throw it. Towards dawn I felt so hungry I contemplated eating a spoonful of tinted face cream.

I was just sinking into a troubled sleep when Jane came in with tea.

I GOT up and dressed quickly. I couldn't stand another minute in this place.

After breakfast Jane made a little sugary speech about how lovely it had been to have me, and I agreed it would be nice if I could come down again. Jane had already sent for the village taxi, and the sound of a car drawing up outside made me gather up my bag, and gloves and make for the front door.

Jane opened it before I got there, and I heard her say surprised, "Why, George, what are you doing here?"

"I'm standing in for Dad," a man's deep voice answered. "He wanted the day off. Where are you going to so early in the day? Dad said I was to step on it."

Jane laughed. "It's my cousin that needs a taxi. She's got to rush back to London."

Then I found myself facing the taxi-driver — and looking into the dreamiest brown eyes.

"Just my luck! I heard you'd arrived from old Tom Parker." George smiled at me. "He's the one who brought you out here."

Suddenly we were the only two people in the world, standing there on Jane's doorstep. I never dreamed it could happen just like that.

"I've changed my mind," I said to Jane. "I'll stay — if you'll have me."

I looked around, seeing for the first time the beauty of the countryside, bathed in the golden glow of morning sunshine, and hearing for the first time the music in the chirruping of the birds . . .

What a wonderful place to be. I love the country!

I still do — when George is with me!

The End.

71

Oh, My Hat !

Complete Story by PAT LACEY

I AM not normally a "hat" person. My nearest approach is a pair of ear muffs in winter and a straw, pot-shaped thing for the garden in summer.

The particular piece of delicate frivolity in question was placed on my head one sunny, summer's morning in a moment of idiocy by the friend who was supposed to be buying one, and it well nigh changed my life.

It really made me look quite attractive — basically a sort of floppy boater, with a wreath of gay flowers on one side, wisps of veiling, and other haberdashery.

"But when should I wear it?" I said weakly as my friend took out *my* cheque book from *my* handbag — it was the cheque book sort of price tag. "The opportunity would never occur."

"You don't wait for the opportunity," my friend said firmly, generously unscrewing her own fountain pen. "You go out and *make* it!"

So there I was, Pru Parfitt — on the eight-ten in my best white summer dress — and The Hat — en route to the office.

Naturally, I had with me the old, plastic holdall in which I carry my lunch sandwiches, my flask, my library book, and my knitting.

I got into my usual carriage and took out my book. It happened to be "Teach Yourself German In Ten Easy Lessons."

"No!" The Hat said, shaking a blue cornflower emphatically.

I got out my knitting, which actually looked more like woven barbed wire — a sort of double, double, chunky double-knit.

"Good heavens, no!" said The Hat.

I meekly put the barbed wire back into its bag.

For lack of something else to do, I gazed at the man who sat opposite me for most of the eight-tens of the preceding six months and found him fixing me with a distinctly wolfish gleam in his eye.

Hitherto he had rarely lifted his eyes from the cricket scores or racing results, according to season. Quite definitely I felt a distinct pressure against my right knee — it was another knee — and not my left one!

What I think is normally described as a "winning smile" appeared on his face. It won him nothing — except an icy stare — until The Hat took over.

"No man," it said, presumably through the trumpet of a gold daffodil nodding at its side, "not even a 'knee-knocker,' should be treated as he deserves. Otherwise you will face a manless existence for the rest of your life. Let's face it — they are necessary beasts."

The icy stare turned into a sort of sultry smirk straight from the perfume-laden bowers of the exotic East.

By the time we reached Euston he was suggesting drinks and a later train that evening. At this point The Hat showed a surprisingly strict,

Without it, she was simply Prue, the girl nobody noticed. When she was wearing it — well, that was different, that was entirely different!

moral attitude — probably a wisp of honesty tucked unseasonably next to the daffodil.

I found myself saying firmly:

"But surely your wife expects you at the usual time?" (Collapse of wolf and virtuous nodding of honesty.)

SOON after leaving the train, the plastic holdall, quite without precedent, was lodged in the Left Luggage Department — The Hat didn't care for sandwiches.

It was then that the great event occurred.

By this time I was sadly late for the office — a line of taxis looked inviting. Even more inviting was a tall, young man in conversation with the leading taxi-driver.

As The Hat moved into his line of vision he broke off his instructions to the driver.

"Could I possibly drop you?" he said. "I'm going in the Piccadilly direction."

"How kind!" murmured The Hat. "That would be most convenient."

Poor, ignorant thing — how was it to know that the office was in the City? — and it climbed into the taxi still with me sitting innocently beneath it.

And so my day of deception began! I had enough presence of mind to telephone a friend to telephone the office to say that I was not myself — (how true!) — and would not be in that day.

Once having abandoned discretion, there was no end to it.

It wasn't so much what I said as what I didn't say — what I managed to imply, and assent to, by my silence.

"What a gorgeous hat! Did you buy it for Ascot?"

"Er, no, we didn't manage Ascot this year." It sounded as if I'd gone last year, and the year before that — and simply nothing would hold me back from next year.

"Up for a day's shopping?"

"You could call it that." The only thing that was stopping me was two days to pay day and two pounds in my purse.

But The Hat got a word in here. "What I'd really like," I heard myself saying, "is a new suit to go with this hat."

Really! So my best grey isn't good enough for you, I thought.

"It's a stunning hat," he said, gazing adoringly at the top of my head as if it were sporting the entire collection of Crown Jewels.

You couldn't say that any of the conversation showed a particularly high level of intelligence, but at the same time we were definitely attracted — all three of us!

IT seemed the natural thing to have a coffee once we arrived in Piccadilly — I needed one.

Coffee led to the suggestion of lunch — he had an appointment in the meantime — and so one o'clock found us seated in one of those gorgeous restaurants full of plush decor where to merely eat seems an impertinence.

Once seated, Bob — his name was Bob Armitage — leaned towards me and asked confidentially, "Have you often been here before?"

74

For some reason, possibly because I had developed a headache, I decided this was the moment to confess all.

I took off The Hat, put it firmly on the seat next to mine and turned to face Bob Armitage, determined to tell him the truth about myself even though it would mean I'd never see him again.

I began preparing my speech in my mind when Bob interrupted.

"That's better — without your hat, I mean!"

I bridled. I couldn't help it. Whatever I might think about The Hat — it was my property. No-one else had the right to criticise it.

He saw my expression and apologies made him almost incoherent.

"Please understand me — it's the most gorgeous hat I have ever seen, and when I saw you walking towards me in the station yard, you looked like the Rites of Spring.

"Not to have smiled at you would have been unnatural and ungrateful. Anyway, I needed you. But going out with someone in a hat like that is like drinking champagne for breakfast — not that I ever have!

"It makes me terribly proud, but terribly tongue tied. Now that you've taken it off I can really talk to you."

One point only stood out clearly in my mind.

"Why," I asked, "did you need me?"

He explained everything.

A PPARENTLY, the appointment, he had had that morning was for a job — and it was terribly important to him that he should get it.

"And, thanks to you, I think I've landed it. When you accepted my invitation out to lunch it really gave me a boost. I felt I could manage any job after that — and from what they said after my interview they agreed with me!

"But the point is I've no right to be taking someone like you out to lunch — I haven't any ready money at all. I've got parents to help to support and I probably won't earn really big money for ages."

Having stated his position in the blackest and most pessimistic terms, he looked at me with a face full of hope.

I gave him the largest smile in my repertoire and opened my mouth to tell him how pleased I was at his bad news.

For the second time in ten minutes speech was denied me. A supercilious creature materialised before us and indicated that it would condescend to take our order.

I smiled at it sweetly, glanced at my watch and rose to my feet.

"I'm afraid we can't wait any longer. We've waited fifteen minutes already."

This was quite true — although I had a feeling that they had been the most important fifteen minutes of my life.

I hissed at Bob as we stalked out (he looking rather bewildered).

"Hope you don't mind, but there's a nice cheap and cheerful coffee bar next door — I use it quite a lot!"

"Excuse me, madam," a voice said, "is this *your* hat?"

I almost denied it and left it there, and then I thought: It could come in rather useful — a super going-away hat!

The End.

SHE had always been just a name to me.

Sally. The girl who had been Paul's girl for so long. The girl who had jilted him the week before their wedding. The girl whose place I had taken. Or — had I? Was I really Paul's girl?

Suddenly, sickeningly, I wasn't sure. His ring was on my left hand, our wedding was planned for spring. And Sally had come back!

Paul hadn't said anything to me, but he must know, everyone knew. It's a small country town, where everyone knows everyone else. And the name on everyone's lips.

"Have you heard Sally Harris is back?"

"Did you know —"

"You'll never guess who I saw —"

No-one had said it to me. Not yet. But soon they would, and I didn't know what I would say, what I would do.

Funny, I didn't even know what she looked like. She had gone a year before I came, and although I'd heard lots of people speak of her, somehow, after Paul's ring was on my finger, they didn't mention Sally any more.

At first, after I knew I wanted Paul, I wondered about Sally. I had a feeling she was tall and blonde. I don't quite know why. I'm dark haired, and — well, I've never exactly been short of boyfriends. But the moment I saw Dr Paul Low — I knew he was the man I'd been waiting for.

He was different from any of the men I'd known. He wasn't very good looking, his face was brown and sort of craggy. He didn't smile very often, but when he did, well, it was his smile that knocked me for six.

I'd come down to spend a weekend with my folk, who'd just retired here. London was my kind of place, not a sleepy little town miles from anywhere.

But I came down to please Mum and Dad, and Dr Low walked into my life. I forgot the civil airline pilot, I forgot the rising young businessman. I forgot everyone but Paul. He was the man for me, and the sooner he knew it the better.

My real chance came when Paul needed a receptionist. He asked for a nurse, but there wasn't much chance of that, and I could type, so I got the job.

At first it was strictly an employer-employee relationship. Then one evening after a particularly busy surgery he invited me for a drink.

Again I saw a different side of this fascinating man — relaxed, humorous, fun to be with.

After that we saw a lot of each other after work. We went dancing,

**Complete Story by
ISOBEL
STEWART.**

76

moonlit drives — and all the time I was so sure I was healing the terrible hurt this faceless girl had inflicted on him.

Then one breathtaking night he proposed, and the date of our wedding was set for April.

So there we were. Paul and I engaged to be married, and all at once this Sally loomed out of his past.

IN fact, Sally couldn't have been further from my thoughts that afternoon when I called the next patient into the surgery.

She was a small girl, smaller than me, with brown, floppy sort of hair, and a little freckled nose. She smiled, and it was the kind of smile that makes you smile right back. I had a card ready to fill in, and I asked for her name.

"It's not really about myself," she said a little breathlessly. "It's my grandfather. He's ill, and — and I came to see him, and I don't know what's wrong with him. I've been so worried."

I could see now she'd been crying.

"I can imagine," I said. "And you wanted to ask Doctor Low just what the position is?"

She nodded, and smiled. A strange, almost shy smile.

"I'll just ask him," I said. "What's the name?"

Her eyes met mine, and I had time to notice that they were a clear grey.

"Harris — Sally Harris."

"We looked at each other for a moment then I felt a surge of relief. It's all right, I thought. If this is his Sally, then I've nothing to worry about. She had an old raincoat on, hardly any make-up, and her hair kept falling over her face. She couldn't have been more plain.

"I'm sure that will be all right," I said levelly, and showed her to the surgery.

I opened the door for Sally to go in and just before I closed it, I heard the silence. I know it's a silly thing to say, but I did. It was such a powerful silence that I heard it.

BUT SALLY ☐AME BACK!

— And that was when Lynn's heartbreak began.

Then I heard Sally give a quick, indrawn breath — and the door clicked shut.

I went back to my desk and began some filing, but I couldn't concentrate. I could hear the rise and fall of the voices through the partition and my heartbeat seemed to fill my whole body and mind.

When they came out, Sally's face was white, and her head high. And Paul — his mouth was set and his eyes cold.

Surely if she didn't matter to him, if he'd forgotten he had ever loved her — surely he wouldn't look like that?

I bent my head over the fypewriter, but Paul brought her across.

"Lynn, this is Sally Harris. Sally — my fiancee, Lynn Harper."

I smiled at Sally Harris and told her I was pleased to meet her, and she smiled back and hoped we'd be very happy.

She left after that, and I wondered what Paul would say — if he would make any mention of what she had once been to him.

But he turned away briskly and said he was going out on his rounds.

After he'd gone I had a lot to think about. And I decided maybe it was just as well Sally Harris had come back. Now Paul would never have any doubts, no lingering memories of her. She was his yesterday, and I was his today and tomorrow and all the days to come.

So, whenever I saw Sally in the shops, at church, in the street, I smiled to her and often stopped to speak. Because I was really quite grateful to her for coming back and laying the ghost once and for all.

A ND then one night, a night of storm and rain and thunder, when I had phoned my folk to say I'd have supper at Paul's then come home after evening surgery, I learned the truth about what Paul felt for Sally Harris.

Paul was out on call, and I was helping his housekeeper, Mrs Mason, get supper ready. There was a knock at the door, and when I opened it, Sally was standing there in the rain, white and exhausted and soaked.

"Paul?" she asked. And the way she said his name told me all I needed to know.

"Come in," I said. "I'm afraid Paul's out."

"It's my grandfather. I — I think he's dying." She drew a swift, ragged breath. "Can't you phone Paul and ask him to come?"

I told her the lines were down here, too, as well as her own — that was why she had had to come.

"You could try Brown's place, or the inn, Sally," Mrs Mason put in quickly, not looking at me. "I heard him say that was where he was going."

I was annoyed to find myself colouring. I should have suggested that.

I pulled on my raincoat. "I'll go to Brown's then."

The rain was driving, and I was soaked right away. It wasn't far to Brown's place, but they told me Paul had gone. I hesitated, then I turned and made for the Harris cottage, beside the inn.

Sally opened the door to me. "Did you find Paul?" I asked.

She shook her head. Then, without another word, she went back through to the bedroom.

I stood in the kitchen, my raincoat dripping, wondering what to do. As I hesitated, there was a quick knock on the door, and Paul came in.

I don't think he even saw me, because Sally stood at the other door, looking at him.

Then she was in his arms, and when I saw the way he held her close to him, the way his cheek rested against her hair — I knew that he had never stopped loving her.

"Oh, Paul," Sally murmured. "He's in such pain, and he's so tired. I — I think he's going."

For a long moment they stood there, and then Sally lifted her chin, and turned to go into the bedroom. Paul went with her, and — and I don't think either of them had even realised I was there.

I stood for a long time, and then suddenly I shivered . . . I was very cold, and very wet. Quickly I went out of the cottage and started to walk home. I suppose there was still a storm. I don't know.

M Y mother was waiting up when I got home. She took one look at me, and took my raincoat off, dried my hair, and sat me down at the fire as if I was nine instead of 19.

When I was drinking a cup of hot chocolate, she said quietly:

"Are you going to tell me what's wrong, Lynn?"

I stared into the fire.

"Paul's in love with that girl," I said at last.

She didn't say anything, and I looked up at her.

"You knew," I said, wonderingly. "And you didn't tell me."

She sighed. "I didn't really know, I just —" She looked at me steadily. "I just knew he wasn't in love with you."

"But he asked me to marry him," I said, and my voice shook.

I looked down at my hand, and twisted the ring. The stone turned round, so that it looked like a wedding ring. I stared at it for a long time, and then I knew.

When I met my mother's eyes I could see she knew, too.

"You're not going to give him up?" she said.

"No, I'm not going to give him up."

Suddenly the hot tears were running down my cheeks. "Why should I? If she hadn't come back we would have got married."

"And — and if he asks you to set him free?"

I shook my hand. "He won't ask me," I said slowly, feeling a cold, hard knot form somewhere inside me.

"He's been jilted himself; he won't do it to me. Oh, if I wanted to break our engagement that would suit him, but he won't jilt me."

I didn't see much of Sally after that, and, consciously at least, I began to think I'd been wrong. There had been a flu epidemic, and Paul was busy; he hardly had any free time, and when he did he was too tired to do anything.

He really did look tired, and I told myself it was tiredness and over-work that made him sit silently beside me when he should have been taking me in his arms.

One night, when I'd stayed on after evening surgery, he had an unexpected call out.

It was more than an hour till he came back. I made him a cup of tea, and while he drank it I sat on the floor with my head against his knee. When he'd finished I sat on the couch beside him, and after a while I thought angrily, if he isn't going to kiss me, then I'm going to kiss him.

Halfway through the kiss Paul took over. His lips bruised mine, and he crushed me in his arms. He kissed me almost desperately. Then he let me go, and after a moment he kissed me again gently.

"I'm sorry, Lynn," he said.

I knew that he didn't mean he was sorry for kissing me like that. He was sorry because he didn't love me.

Part of me wanted to say there and then that if he didn't want me then I didn't want him, and he could go to his Sally. But my lips were still bruised from his kiss, and I knew that I wanted Paul at any price.

So I said nothing.

But that night I woke to find my pillow wet with tears. Suddenly I was angry. No man had ever made me cry before, and I wasn't going to cry now. If only that girl would go, I told myself, everything would be fine.

While I thought that, I knew what I was going to do. The next day, at lunchtime, I went along to see Sally Harris.

S HE was tidying out books and papers. In the last few weeks she had grown thinner, and her eyes were sad.

She didn't seem surprised to see me. We sat down at the fire. She apologised for the untidiness.

"I have to get everything sorted out now, and — and my grandfather had lived here all his life."

I wanted to say I was sorry about her grandfather, but somehow I couldn't — not when I knew what I was going to say next.

"And — after you've finished?" I asked, deliberately cool.

"Then I'll go," she said quietly. "Will you be happier then?"

I hadn't quite expected this, but I answered her coolly.

"Yes, I will. It's — unsettling to have you around when Paul and I are busy making wedding plans."

I'd thought she was shy, retiring, unable to stand up for herself. But she looked at me squarely, with flames of colour in her cheeks.

"You know that Paul and I love each other?" she said clearly.

Her eyes met mine, and suddenly all pretence was gone. All at once I knew I had to be honest with this girl. I don't know why, but I had to.

"All right," I said, "I know Paul loves you, and I know you love him. And — I'm still wearing his ring; I'm still making wedding plans. Until Paul himself asks me to —"

"You know Paul would never ask you to set him free."

"Look," I said impatiently. "The way I look at it, you lost all rights to Paul when you jilted him and went away. Why should you come back and take up where you left off?"

"That's what Paul wanted to know," she said at last.

"Paul and I have known each other all our lives. We grew up together, we've always been friends, and — gradually, we knew we were in love with each other. Then — just before the wedding, I began to have doubts. I — I suppose every bride has them.

"Neither of us had ever been in love with anyone else. We had never kissed anyone else, never really known anyone else. And — and I began to wonder if we were being fair to ourselves, fair to each other.

"I — I realised I couldn't go through with it. So I ran away. I had

                                    Continued on page 82

I DO like people. Honest I do. They're so good at opening milk bottles and tinned cat food.

"But possibly I like cats best. We're so intelligent, so clean and fastidious, so — well, let's face it, we're so superior.

"And of course many of us are pedigreed. Well, no, I'm not. But my mother, bless her sharp claws, knew a good Persian when she met him.

"It's true we're not so appreciative of people as we are of food, warmth and comfort. But just the same we can be very affectionate.

"We ask so little, just a place to call our own between hunting and exploring forays — and, of course, some nice big gardens or fields in which to foray!

"If you don't have a cat try one of us. So dignified, so aloof, so quiet and relaxed. We don't ask much of anybody. Just their home . . ."

OCCUPATIONAL HAZARDS
Milkmen going on strike.
Owners who don't like dead mice.
Holiday-time for people.

MOTTO
Drinkapintamilkaday.

I LIKE PEOPLE

tried to make Paul see things the same way, but it wasn't any use."

She looked at me defiantly. "I know I shouldn't have done it that way, but — I was young, and I was so mixed up about everything."

She looked down at her bare left hand. Involuntarily I looked at my left hand, with the square sapphire gleaming on it.

"I knew very soon I'd made a mistake. I knew my heart had been right, and not my head. There — there was just Paul for me."

"Have you told Paul this?"

"Yes, I told him. He — he understands why I did it."

She looked at me levelly. "But none of this makes any difference to you, Lynn. You're still hanging on to Paul.

"Why Paul?" she asked curiously. "You — with your looks — you could have any man you wanted."

"Paul happens to be the man I want," I said. "That's all there is to it."

P AUL was sitting at his desk when I went in, staring blindly at the blotter. He looked up.

"I've just been to see Sally," I said evenly. "I'd like to tell you what I've just told her."

I took a deep breath. Now or never, I told myself. I took the ring from my hand and held it out to him.

"I know there's an occasional bit of excitement like this," I said lightly, laughingly. "But — but, Paul, I'm afraid I'm not really cut out to be a small town girl. I — I'd be bored stiff in a month here. I'm sorry, but — but I want to go back to London."

I met his eyes and for a moment I could feel the tears threatening.

"Let's consider our engagement broken, Paul. No hard feelings — just you go your way and I'll go mine."

And I'll never see you again, my darling, I thought, with sudden stabbing pain. Because I couldn't bear to.

"What can I say," Paul's voice was harsh and unsteady. "I was sure when you understood, that —"

"That I wouldn't make a doctor's wife? You're right, Paul."

My pride was all I had left, and I was hanging on to that.

"Goodbye, Paul. I — I won't come back. I'll probably go tomorrow." I went out then, without looking back.

I'll go back tomorrow, I thought. I've been away too long . . . it will be great being in London again. I've missed the parties, the night-clubs, and all the dates . . .

But I knew that if Paul had loved me, I would willingly have lived all the rest of my life anywhere that he wanted. And suddenly I knew I would never again be able to love lightly.

I knew, even then, that some time, there would be someone else for me. But it wouldn't be for quite a while.

Only when I found a man who came first with me, and who held me first with him — then I would love again.

And — because I'd loved Paul, he would have to be very special.

Alone in the quiet village street I tried to smile. He would be worth waiting for, the man I would love.

The End.

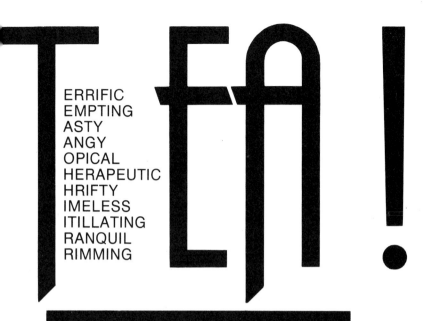

TEA!

ERRIFIC
EMPTING
ASTY
ANGY
OPICAL
HERAPEUTIC
HRIFTY
IMELESS
ITILLATING
RANQUIL
RIMMING

New Ways With An Old Favourite

DID you know tea accounts for half of everything we drink in Britain — excluding tap water? Every man, woman and child over the age of 10 drinks an average of four cups of tea a day!

After 20 years of decline, tea consumption is now rising steadily. Young people in particular have suddenly realised what an economic, healthy and refreshing drink it is.

IT'S ECONOMICAL

A 125 gram packet of leaf tea makes, on average, 55 cups of tea. A 250 gram packet of tea bags contains 80 tea bags which will make between 100-150 cups of tea, depending on how strong you like it.

Even taking into account the price rises earlier this year, that's still a jolly cheap cuppa!

IT'S HEALTHY

Tea is a natural drink; it contains no additives, no flavouring, no colouring, no artificial chemicals. And if you drink it with lemon, leaving out the sugar and milk — no Calories!

Tea also contributes to your vitamin intake and that of Mangenese, Zinc, Potassium and Magnesium. It's a source of Fluoride. It's low in Sodium, as is appropriate for salt-free diets. There are no carbohydrates or fat if served without milk or sugar.

A warming cup of hot, sweet tea is well known as a calming influence in a crisis. It can also help you sleep at night by reducing tension and helping you relax.

83

SUMMERTIME REFRESHERS

Iced tea was "discovered" by an
glishman trying to sell cups of tea
the public at the world exhibition in
Louis, U.S.A., in 1904. There was
heatwave on at the time, no-one
as interested in the hot drink —
ey all passed by looking for some-
ng cold. In desperation, he put ice
bes in the tea — and iced tea was
rn.

To obtain a clear amber liquid
hich is attractive to look at and
ean and refreshing to drink:
Fill a glass jug with cold water and
add two tea bags for each pint.
Cover the jug and place in the
refrigerator for at least eight hours
(or overnight).
Remove the tea bags and pour into
tall glasses. Your iced tea is ready
to drink.

SPICED CIDER PUNCH

pint iced tea   Few cloves
lemons, sliced   1 pint sweet cider
cinnamon sticks   Sugar to taste
Pour iced tea over sliced lemons,
nnamon sticks and cloves. Allow to
eep for 1 hour. Add cider and sugar
taste. Serve chilled. Serves 8-10.

STRAWBERRY FAYRE

pint iced tea   Sugar to taste
pint sparkling white wine
rawberries and mint sprigs to garnish
Pour iced tea and well-chilled white
ine together and pour into tall
lasses. Garnish with sliced straw-
erries and mint sprigs. Serve well
illed. Serves 8-10.

IN THE PICTURE
Back: Strawberry Fayre.
2nd Row: Russian Roulette,
Tea Fizz, Rum Cup.
3rd Row: Veranda Fruit Cup,
Spiced Cider Punch,
Front: Planter's Punch.

TEA FIZZ

1 pint iced tea   ¼ pint lime cordial
1 pint lemonade   Lime slices to garnish
Mix tea, lemonade and lime juice
together, garnish with lime slices.
Serve well chilled. Serves 10.

VERANDA FRUIT CUP

1 pint iced tea   ¼ pint orange cordial
½ pint soda water   ¼ pint lemon juice
2 x 6 oz. bottles ginger ale
Assorted fruits to garnish   Sugar to taste
Mix tea, ginger ale, soda water,
lemon juice and orange cordial
together. Add sugar to taste. Garnish
glasses with assorted fruits. Serve
well chilled. Serves 10-12.

PLANTERS PUNCH

1 pint iced tea   ¼ pint brandy
1 pint clear sparkling orange juice
¼ pint clear lemon juice .
Apple, lemon and orange slices to garnish.
Mix tea, apple juice, lemon juice
and brandy together. Add sliced fruit
to garnish. Serve well chilled.
Serves 12.

RUM CUP

1 pint iced tea   ½ pint lemonade
¼ pint orange cordial   ¼ pint dark rum
Orange slices to garnish Sugar to taste
Mix tea, lemonade, rum and
orange cordial together and add
sugar to taste. Pour into glasses and
garnish with orange slices. Serve
well chilled. Serves 8-10.

RUSSIAN ROULETTE

¼ pint iced tea   Lime slices to garnish
¼ pint lime cordial ¼ pint vodka
Crushed ice
Mix tea, vodka and lime cordial
together. Pour over crushed ice and
garnish glasses with fresh lime
slices. Serves 5-6.

85

MAKING A CUPPA

1. Fill the kettle with freshly-drawn water from the *cold* tap. Why? The water will be fresh and aerated, which brings out the full flavour of tea.
2. Pre-heat the teapot with very hot water and empty it away before adding the water. Why? A warm pot means the water stays at boiling point when it comes into contact with the tea.
3. Use one bag or spoon of tea per person and one for the pot. Why? No-one likes insipid tea.
4. When the water is boiling vigorously, bring the teapot to the kettle (so the water stays boiling) and then pour over the tea. Why? Water which is not quite boiling produces thin, weak tea. Over-boiled water produces a muddy, bitter brew, due to oxygen loss.
5. Let the tea brew for 5 minutes, then stir. Why? This is the time needed for all the properties of the tea to be extracted. If brewed longer, strength and colour will overwhelm flavour. If brewed for less time, the colour will be there, but the flavour will be lacking.
6. Serve. With milk and sugar — or lemon, if preferred. MIF. Milk In First, then add sugar to individual taste. Don't use too much — milk and sugar cost more than tea!

Lemon Tea

Make slightly weaker. Then pour into a cup over a slice of lemon. Or try two fresh sprigs of SAGE . . . or a sprig of fresh MINT . . .

POINTS TO REMEMBER!

★ Don't let tea "stew" in the pot for any length of time — certainly not more than 10 minutes.
★ We all get used to the water we drink and then when we go on holiday we notice it tastes "different." So tea will taste different, too. Hard water can make the tea cloudy, and cause a thin surface skin to form. It can also impair aroma and taste. Tea made with *naturally* soft water usually has a more golden colour. However, *artificially* softened water (from a water softener) spoils tea by giving a muddy appearance and unpleasant taste. So it's always best to use water direct from the mains.

WARM UP WITH TEA

PLANTERS TEA PUNCH

1 litre Twinings Assam Tea
1 pint dark rum
½ pint orange juice
¼ pint lemon juice
Soft brown sugar
Lemon and orange slices

Place tea, rum and orange juice together in a saucepan. Heat through but do not boil. Add lemon juice and soft brown sugar to taste. Float lemon and orange slices on top to decorate and serve piping hot.

Makes approximately 10 servings.

SCOTCH MIST

¾ pint Twinings Ceylon Tea
½ pint whisky
3-4 teaspoonfuls clear honey
A little double cream

Place tea and whisky together in a saucepan. Add honey and heat through, but do not boil. Pour into coffee cups and float a little cream on top. Serve after dinner.

Serves 4.

GINGER UP

¾ pint Twinings Darjeeling Tea
¾ pint apple juice
2 teaspoonfuls ground ginger
Brown sugar to taste

Mix tea and apple juice together in a saucepan. Add ground ginger and brown sugar to taste. Heat, but do not boil. Pour into 4 glasses.

Serves 4.

SPICED LEMON TEA

1 slice of lemon
4 cloves
1 pint of freshly-made Twinings Earl Grey Tea
4 tablespoonfuls fresh lemon juice
Sugar to taste
4 cinnamon sticks to garnish
4 lemon slices to garnish.

Stud lemon slices with cloves and place in a pot of freshly-made tea. Infuse for 3 minutes and remove. Place 1 x 15 ml spoon/1 tablespoonful of lemon juice in each of the 4 glasses and top up with tea. Sweeten to taste and serve each with a cinnamon stick and slice of lemon to garnish.

Serves 4.

WHERE BRITAIN'S TEA COMES FROM

BANGLADESH
INDIA
KENYA
OTHER AFRICA
INDONESIA
TANZANIA
SRI LANKA
MOZAMBIQUE
CHINA
U.S.S.R.
MALAWI
ARGENTINA
REST OF THE WORLD

87

WHAT KIND OF TEA?

WE ought to be fussier about tea. We don't experiment enough. Why not have two kinds of tea in the larder? An everyday blend, and a super-fine one for special occasions?

Most of the packets of tea at your local supermarket are blends. Sometimes as many as 30 different teas from different countries are used to arrive at a good quality tea, which tastes just as the public wants, and can be sold at an economic price. Most popular brands contain three basic elements — North Indian tea for strength and pungency; Ceylon tea for flavour and colour; and African, especially Kenya, for colour and brightness. Other teas are used to balance the blend so that a particular brand will taste the same throughout the year.

Packet or tea bag? The tea in popular brands of tea bags is exactly the same quality as that in packet tea. The smaller leaf dye is chosen to give the faster infusion (ideally, allow three minutes).

Speciality Teas

India is the largest tea producer. Teas from **Assam** are rich and full with a strong flavour; an ideal breakfast tea. **Darjeeling** teas are grown in the foothills of the Himalayas with a delicate "Muscatel" flavour and an exquisite bouquet; known as the champagne of teas. **Nilgiri** comes from the Nilgiri Hills of Southern India and is light, "bright" and delicate in taste.

From Sri Lanka come the Ceylon teas with their pale golden colour and good flavour. **Dimbula** is grown 4000 feet above sea level and has a typical flavour and golden colour. **Nuwara Eliya** is a delicate, light "bright" tea with a fragrant flavour; excellent with lemon. **Uva** is a fine-flavoured tea fromn the eastern slopes of the Central Mountains.

Africa producers **Kenya** — Bright Liquoring Teas with a particularly refreshing character; a good all-round tea.

In the 17th century China was our sole supplier, but is now of minority interest. China teas are generally bright with distinctive flavours. **Keemum** comes from Anwhei province; is light, delicate and ideal with Chinese food. **Lapsang Souchong** is a pungent tea with a smokey flavour and aroma; an exotic and unusual taste, best served without milk.

From the Orient comes **Jasmine** — a scented tea containing jasmine petals which produces a light liquer with an exotic fragrance and flavour. Also **Formosa Oolong** which is the world's most expensive tea (£12 a ton — about 5p a cup!) with a light liquor reminiscent of peach blossom.

If you fancy a smart blend, there's **Earl Grey** which is traditionally a blend of teas from Darjeeling and China, scented with the citrus oil of bergamot. The epitome of genteel afternoon tea can be enjoyed with or without milk. **English Breakfast** is an established blend of North India and Ceylon teas, providing a full-flavoured, rich and satisfying beverage.

Shelf Life and Storage. Tea can be stored for quite a while although the flavour can deteriorate with time. It's best to buy regularly. Tea can absorb moisture and smells. Keep it away from detergents, fruit, coffee — or anything scented. Keep in traditional caddy in a cool place.

I LIKE PEOPLE

BUT I'm not so sure I like other dogs. They're so much "nose-in-the-air" types. I tell you straight it's frustrating when you can't say hello without the use of a step-ladder.

And my sense of humour — and we dachshunds are noted for our zest for fun — does not extend to, "What's the weather like down there?" and "Be careful the grass doesn't scratch you too much!"

Life is rather difficult for us, when you consider the height of modern arm-chairs and settees. What's a casual step-up for other dogs is a Grand National jump for us.

But we manage!

Sometimes I wish my legs were just a little longer. I wish that most when I'm taken for a walk. Oh, you long-legged people!

But there's one thing you ought to know about us. Our shapes may be — er — like a sausage, and our legs in need of a good leg-pull (which we get much too often) but we're game dogs when it comes to badger-hunting or getting down a rabbit hole. Just try us!

And there's not much that goes on without us getting to hear about it . . . which goes to prove that having an ear to the ground (and we have two!) is a good thing!

The No-Fuss, No-F

**— At least it was meant to be . . .
until the village heard the young couple's
plans!**

I'M not having a white wedding, Mum, and that's that!"
With a determined nod, Anne Wetherill perched her five-foot-
nothing on the arm of her fiance's chair and took his hand.

Mrs Wetherill sighed and lowered her knitting. "But Anne, dear, I've
always looked forward to a white wedding for you. And, besides, in
church, what looks lovelier? The whole village will be there to see it,
you know."

"Oh no they won't!" Anne retorted. "Because we're not having a
church wedding. We're getting married in the registry office at
Monksbury — aren't we, Trevor?"

Trevor Blakesley nodded and made a non-committal sound. He
seemed suddenly fascinated by the design on the hearth rug.

"Not having . . ." Mrs Wetherill's knitting dropped on her lap and a
needle tinkled on to the tiled hearth. "Not having a church wedding?
But, Anne — you were christened in the village church, you went to
Sunday school there, you were confirmed there. And the vicar —
what will the vicar say? He'll be terribly put out."

"Mum, what the vicar says doesn't really matter. This is our affair —
our own private affair, Mum — and it's nothing to do with the rest of
the village. I'll be married in a suit or a simple dress and we can have a
quiet tea in a hotel in town, with just you and Trevor's family there.
That's the way we want it, Mum."

THE next day was Saturday. During the week Anne worked in an
office in Monksbury, but on Saturday mornings she helped her
mother in the village post office-cum-shop.

To her surprise a few of the earlier customers congratulated her on
her engagement. She didn't know how they'd found out so soon — but
she might have known that in a village it wouldn't take long for the news
to get around.

She was just thinking about taking a breather when the bell over the
door tinkled and old Mr Baines came in.

He was a widower who lived alone and Mrs Wetherill sometimes took
pity on the lonely old man and invited him over for a meal.

"Well, lass," he grunted affably, "they tell me you're getting wed.
'Bout time, too. Can you cook and wash and clean? No good getting wed
if you can't, you know!"

Complete Story by V. TURNBULL

Anne smiled. The old man had a gruff manner but she'd always liked him.

He was fumbling for something in the inside pocket of his rather shabby jacket. Finally he drew out a small parcel, which he pushed under the grille to Anne. She picked it up to put it on to the post office scales, but the old man stopped her.

"Nay, lass, that's not for posting. It's a present for you."

Anne looked at the old man in surprise as he went on: "You and your mother have been kind to me, lass, and it's meant a lot to me. An' this means a lot to me, too — it belonged to my Jane. I gave it to her when we was courtin'. Saved up for it for months, I did."

He chuckled to himself. "They're not real, of course, but they were decent quality, and they'll look so nice on a white wedding dress."

Before Anne could speak the old man had turned and left the shop.

She opened the parcel and found a case of imitation red leather. Inside was a pearl necklace and a time-worn plate with the inscription: *To my Jane. The best wife in the world.*

HALFWAY through the morning there was a slight commotion at the door. Anne went to open it, for this usually meant Mrs Wingfield was trying to get in.

Sure enough, there was the frail, silver-haired old lady in her wheelchair, with her almost equally frail old husband trying to open the post office door and raise his wife's chair up the two steps.

Anne smiled. "Can I get you anything, Mrs Wingfield?"

The old woman looked up at her. She had been a cripple for years and the rumour in the village was that she would never be able to leave her wheelchair. Her husband was always by her side, wheeling her wherever she wanted to go.

IF I HAD MY WAY

I SUPPOSE that like most grown-ups you are thinking: Look at him! Does nothing but eat and sleep and cry.

Well, you're wrong. I am not sleeping. I'm just resting my eyes and working very hard at a problem. "If it takes a man a week to walk a fortnight, how long does it take a fly to crawl through a small barrel of treacle?"

I often lie and work out simple little brain-teasers like that. Mind you, sometimes it's difficult. Oh, not the problem! Just getting peace to work the darned thing out. There's always a grown-up — or two! — coming in and out and disturbing me. Which is why I'm pretending to be asleep.

If I had my way, I'd make grown-ups work out problems. Important big problems. For example: If a baby wakes at 4 a.m. on a cold winter's night and cries for a feed, at what temperature should be (a) his bottle, (b) his bedroom, and (c) your temper?

Grown-ups wouldn't work at that, you know. Their twisted minds would be working on completely different lines . . . If a baby wakes at 4 a.m. on a cold winter's night, who would attend to the baby if (a) you wouldn't, (b) your husband wouldn't and (c) there was nobody else in the house?

When I'm a grown-up (and that's a fate we all have to suffer!) I know what my big problem will be — convincing other grown-ups that I need so much rest in which to solve all my other problems!

THOUGHT FOR TODAY
The difficult I can think up at once, the impossible takes me a little longer.

Mrs Wingfield's pale blue eyes had an unusual sparkle in them as she held out a very small packet wrapped in tissue paper.

"Open it, dear," she told Anne.

Anne tore aside the wrapping. Inside was a handkerchief of finest white cambric, with an initial "A" delicately embroidered in one corner, and a border of exquisite lace.

"It's hand-made lace, my dear," Mrs Wingfield explained in a confidential whisper. "And I thought since it had the initial 'A' it would be so suitable for you — my name's Alice, you know. It was the handkerchief I carried at my wedding, and I've never used it since . . ."

Suddenly, Anne felt a catch in her throat.

"I never had a daughter of my own to pass it on to," the old woman was saying, her eyes dim with unfulfilled hopes. "I — I always dreamed my daughter would carry it on her wedding day, but — I could never have children, you see . . ."

Anne felt a wave of panic. I'm going to cry, she thought. I'm going to cry . . .

"Anyway," the old woman went on, "it would give me such great pleasure to see you carry it on your wedding day. My husband is going to wheel me up to the church to see you — it will be a very happy day."

THE next day Anne went into Monksbury to visit Trevor's parents. Mrs Blakesley, like Mrs Wetherill, was clearly disappointed that it wasn't to be a church wedding, but she seemed to have made up her mind to accept things and make the best of them.

But Trevor's young sister Susan was more outspoken. She made no attempt to hide her disgust at being deprived of the opportunity of being a bridesmaid at a "real wedding," as she called it.

Trevor himself was very thoughtful, and after tea, when Mrs Blakesley had tactfully taken Susan off to help with the washing-up, he turned to Anne.

"Anne, darling — are you sure we're doing the right thing about the wedding? I mean, about having it in the registry office."

"Oh, Trevor," Anne burst out. "We made up our minds long ago, didn't we? Don't go letting your mum and my mum, and everybody else, talk you into things."

She shook her head. "The trouble about living in a village is that everybody takes too big an interest in your affairs."

"It's only because they're interested, darling."

"I know," Anne said, despairingly. "I know that. That's what makes it so hard to go against them all. But it's nothing to do with anybody else. Don't you see, darling, this wedding is our affair — just yours and mine and nobody else's . . ."

A FEW days later Anne met Major Turvey, a retired Army officer who ran a nursery and market-garden. He slapped her on the back with a heartiness which very nearly sent her staggering.

"Well, Anne, my girl — this is splendid news! Mrs Turvey and myself are delighted. And, Anne . . ." — he dropped his voice to a whisper — "I'm counting on making your wedding bouquet. It'll be the best I've ever made. And flowers for the church, too. You can think of it as our wedding present to you."

"It's very kind of you, Major Turvey," Anne smiled, "but as a matter of fact my fiance and I are planning a very quiet wedding — in the registry office in Monksbury."

For a moment the Major stared at her in utter disbelief, then he threw back his head and roared with laughter.

"Don't tell me you're having wedding nerves already! Still, don't worry, they say all brides go through it. I must confess I was scared stiff myself, until I found myself standing in church.

"I wouldn't have had any other kind of wedding. Gives you something to look back on, and — well — it sort of *cements* your married life. Registry office, indeed!"

"It's nothing to do with nerves, Major Turvey. I . . ."

But he wasn't listening. He slapped Anne on the back again and went off, still chuckling and shaking his head.

THE vicar called several days later to offer his congratulations. Trevor was there when he arrived, and after saying how pleased he was at the engagement, he turned to the question of wedding plans.

Mrs Wetherill gave an embarrassed little cough and Trevor looked as if he wished he was somewhere else.

"I'm sorry, Vicar," Anne said steadily, "we've decided to have a quiet wedding in the registry office. We both prefer it that way."

The vicar stared at her.

"But — do think carefully about it," he said, very gently. "Have a quiet wedding, by all means — but, Anne, you must start your married life together in church, with God's blessing."

Anne shook her head.

"We *have* thought carefully about it, Vicar. I'm really very sorry about it, because everyone seemed to be expecting us to have a church wedding, and they've all been so kind, but . . ."

She broke off as there was a knock at the door. Mrs Wetherill hurried to answer it, looking only too glad to escape for a moment.

When she came back into the room there was another woman with her. "Mrs Smith to see you, Anne."

Anne looked up in surprise. Mrs Smith was a middle-aged widow who lived at Rose Cottage, a few doors along from the post office, and devoted most of her time to her garden and her small dog.

She took no part in any social affairs in the village and had never made any attempt to make friends with anyone — which made her visit all the more surprising.

She walked slowly, hesitantly, into the room, carrying a large, flat cardboard box.

"I'm sorry," she murmured hesitantly, "I hope I'm not intruding? No, no, Vicar — please don't go.

"I've heard the news about your engagement, Miss Wetherill," she went on, rather diffidently, "and I came to wish you happiness, and to bring you this. I hope you won't think it presumptuous . . ." She handed the box to Anne. "I — I hope you'll wear it on your wedding day."

Slowly Anne opened the carefully-tied box, removed layers of white tissue-paper, and lifted out a beautiful bridal veil. There seemed to be yards and yards of it, soft and filmy and white, with lovers' knots embroidered in the corners.

"It was mine." Mrs Smith's usually crisp, rather stern voice had dropped to a near whisper. "My aunt sent it from New York for my wedding.

"It was during the war that we were married, you know, and it wasn't easy to get everything that was needed. I borrowed a white satin dress from a friend. We had to get up to all sorts of dodges in those days!"

Her face lit up in an unexpected smile. Anne couldn't remember ever having seen Mrs Smith smile before, and suddenly she realised that this faded, stern woman must once have been very attractive indeed. She had lovely brown eyes and when she smiled her mouth was soft and pretty. *Continued on page* 97

I LIKE PEOPLE

LIFE is grim, life is hard, life is earnest! And you dear people make it so.

It's not all that much fun being a lap dog. We never get to chase cows all over the fields or trap desperate criminals who have guns, or rescue people from rivers in flood.

We have to put up with being cuddled by glamorous girls who only use the most expensive perfume and who kiss and drool all over us.

It's all very exhausting, you know.

We're not thrown out the back door into the mud and rain. No such luck! We're taken out in big slick cars to find somewhere not so wet and are then brought home to dry our poor little paws before a blazing fire.

It really does tax our strength.

But we're a hardy breed and we can't let down our Chinese ancestors. That's why we go on suffering the way we do.

Now if you'll pardon me, I have a meal waiting and my satin cushion is being warmed by the fire . . .

"You must have looked very lovely," Anne replied in a whisper.

"It *was* a lovely wedding," Mrs Smith said softly. "Hugh was in uniform, of course. He was a Spitfire pilot, and I was so proud of him! We had a . . . a few days' honeymoon in the Lake District, and then he went back."

She was silent for a long time before going on. "A week later he crashed and was killed. We had been so happy . . ."

The room was silent except for the ticking of the clock. Anne, her mother, Trevor and the vicar — they all sat watching the woman they had always thought of as cold and emotionless, waiting for her to speak.

She took out a handkerchief and dabbed at her eyes.

"I had so little time with Hugh, but in all these years I've always had my wedding day to look back on and it's the happiest memory of my life."

She stood up, suddenly seeming to regain some of her usual stiffness.

"Well, I must go . . ." she murmured.

Anne went with her to the door. As the older woman was about to leave she caught her by the arm and, on a sudden impulse, kissed her on the cheek.

"Thank you for the veil," she whispered. "It's a lovely present . . ."

There was complete silence in the living-room when Anne went back in. She felt their eyes on her.

"Vicar," she said very softly, "is it too late to change my mind about the wedding? I'd like to get married in church after all . . ."

THE vicar stood on the chancel step and smiled reassuringly at Trevor, who was standing before him.

At the church door a very excited Susan was helping to arrange the long folds of Mrs Smith's veil. Anne, her cheeks glowing, her eyes sparkling, stood calm and poised, holding her small but beautiful bouquet of Major Turvey's choicest flowers.

Around the neckline of her white brocade dress lay Mr Baine's necklace, and Mrs Wingfield's handkerchief was tucked into one sleeve, the exquisite lace cascading over her hand.

In the front pew, beside her mother and aunt, old Mr Wingfield was sitting, strategically placed with his wife's wheelchair at the end of the pew beside him.

Behind them was Mr Baines, in his carefully-brushed Sunday suit. He beamed joyfully at Anne as she passed.

The Turveys sat near the middle of the church and Anne noticed the bluff, hearty major seek his wife's hand and press it affectionately.

And at the back of the church Mrs Smith sat alone. There were tears on her cheeks, but she was smiling.

At last they reached the chancel step. The vicar smiled happily down at the young couple before him, and in a firm voice addressed the congregation.

"Dearly beloved, we are gathered together here in the sight of God and in the face of this congregation to join together this man and this woman in Holy Matrimony . . ."

The End.

by **BRENDA GOURGEY**

Our Sunday Child

Barry was only five years old, but already he had an adult's awareness of the world — it wasn't going to be easy to gain his friendship . . .

BARRY was just five years old. His face was wistful and serious, his eyes dark and rather sad. He was not quite like other children of his age: he was an orphan.

His mother had died about a year before and his father, unable to care for the boy himself, had placed him in the care of an orphanage.

I first saw Barry through the serving hatch of the house he lived in. It was quite an ordinary house, one of many owned by the orphanage, and in it lived 12 children, cared for by a housemother and housefather.

Barry's head suddenly appeared on the dining-room side of the hatch.

"Hey!" he shouted. "It's my birthday on Saturday."

He smiled, suddenly showing a row of small even white teeth. But his eyes remained soulful and I could sense wariness.

I looked quickly at Mrs Craig,

Barry's housemother, who was standing next to me in the kitchen.

"Come in here, Barry!" she told him. "Meet your auntie!"

"You my auntie?" he asked me.

"If you like."

He seemed to accept the fact without question. Seconds later, he came running out of the dining-room door, took the steps into the kitchen in one bound and stood looking up at me.

"It's my birthday on Saturday," he told me again. "My daddy's giving me a red bus and I'm going to have a party. Mrs Craig's making me a cake with five candles on it."

From his expression, I could see he was sizing me up. Mrs Craig must have sensed my awkwardness for she brought two cups of tea and a plate of biscuits and left Barry and me alone in the lounge.

Very politely, he offered me a biscuit, then took one himself.

"Do you go to school?" he asked suddenly.

"I did once," I replied, relieved that Barry had started a conversation. "Do you?"

"Yes. I don't like it, though." He wrinkled his nose expressively.

I couldn't help feeling discouraged. The conversation was very stilted.

For a moment, I regretted agreeing to the principal's request to become Barry's "aunt." Immediately, of course, I felt ashamed of the thought.

All my husband, Peter, and I would have to do was to have Barry for the day on Sundays and occasionally during school holidays, remember Christmas and his birthday, and generally befriend him.

Spontaneously — though perhaps to atone for the guilty feeling — I said: "What would you like me to give you for your birthday, Barry?"

"A red bus."

"But your daddy's giving you one."

"I know," Barry said. "But he might forget."

I looked at him keenly, but his expression showed that he was quite serious.

B ARRY came to us for the first time the day after his birthday party. He arrived in time for lunch.

All through the meal, he played the little gentleman. He passed the sauce, the salt, the pepper without a murmur. He finished first and sat quietly until the meal was over.

From his set, staid expression and lack of conversation, I concluded with a sinking heart that he was simply waiting resignedly until the day was over and he could go home.

After lunch, when Peter had helped me pile the dishes on to the trolley, Barry followed me into the kitchen, picked up a dishcloth and stood waiting. I made an attempt at conversation.

"Do you like wiping up?" I said, and regretted it as soon as the words were out of my mouth.

"I don't mind," was the reply.

After that, we said nothing. Although I tried to suppress the thought, I found myself hoping the day would pass quickly.

I looked across at Peter, who was standing in the doorway.

"The drawing book," I mouthed at him, "the drawing book."

Peter nodded, I think we were both glad that we had provided something for Barry to do.

"Just in case it rains," I had said to Peter when we were discussing our plans for the day.

We had thought of boating on the river near our home, the children's playground in the park, tea in the riverside restaurant nearby and a few indoor activities in case of bad weather. It had never occurred to either of us that we would be glad to give Barry a drawing book and a box of crayons because we felt so awkward just talking to him.

Barry soon immersed himself in colouring the pictures and adding a few scribbles of his own. I know I felt quite relieved and I think Peter did, too.

"We're probably trying too hard," Peter said, but we both felt disappointed at the way the day seemed to be turning out.

After about 20 minutes, I felt I simply must try again. Peter demurred.

"He's quite happy as he is," he reasoned.

"We're supposed to be entertaining him," I retorted, but secretly I thought Peter was right.

I looked over Barry's shoulder. "Let's see," I said.

Immediately and without a word, Barry obeyed.

"Very nice," I commented, thinking it rather imaginative. He had added a few extra touches to the rather set drawing of a family picnic by the river. Barry had used the crayons skilfully, graduating the colours and differentiating between the leaves of the trees and the green of the bushes that spilled down the bank of the river.

I had a sudden idea.

"Would you like to have a picnic like that?"

I saw a flicker of interest on Barry's face.

Quickly, I packed a hamper with sandwiches, cakes, biscuits and flasks of tea and, with Peter holding Barry's hand, we made our way down to the river.

On the way, we bought Barry a blue yacht and I wrote his name across it in large letters with my lipstick. Barry seemed very pleased.

"Thank goodness," I muttered to Peter, and could see he agreed.

Barry lost even more of his reticence once the boat had pushed away from the shore and was sailing.

"Brrrm, brrm." Barry leaned over, trying to make the boat go faster.

AFTERWARDS, however, Barry seemed to lose some of his recklessness and quietly helped me lay out the picnic. Then he sat munching sandwiches and looking contemplatively out over the water.

"It's nice living by the river, isn't it?" he said. "Very pretty and peaceful." He pointed a finger. "Look at those swans, aren't they lovely?"

It was then I realised what was so disturbing about Barry. He had been behaving like a miniature adult rather than a child. A child, I thought, would have noticed the boats and the people, the ice-cream and balloon-sellers rather than the swans and peaceful atmosphere.

But this wasn't surprising, really. In his brief life, Barry had known more tragedy and upheaval than adults many years his senior. He had had to grow up almost overnight; abruptly his senses must have been sharpened and, being highly intelligent, his awareness of human failings had developed almost too quickly.

Peter glanced at his watch.

"Nearly six, I'm afraid," he said, getting up.

We packed up and walked home along the river bank. There were fewer boats now, fewer people. The evening was closing in and one by one the lights in the town were flickering on. Barry said nothing but kept his eyes on the river as we walked along.

He still seemed thoughtful as Peter unlocked the front door. Then he said: "This is a nice place. Am I going to sleep here?"

I looked across to Peter.

"There's always next Sunday," I said, sensing his disappointment.

"Yes," said Barry resignedly. He shrugged on his coat with a barely audible sigh. His expression betrayed nothing, but perhaps he had in his mind hoped that Peter and I would prove to be rather more permanent in his life and that our home would become his as well.

"Take your drawing book," Peter told him. "Then you can show us the pictures you've drawn during the week."

"All right." Barry spoke without much enthusiasm.

I looked down at the small figure standing so dejectedly in the hall, and felt a rush of pity. With difficulty, I controlled it. It would do Barry no good to part from us this first time with an emotional scene.

I felt I had to do something, so I bent down and put my arms about him. Instinctively, he flinched away from me but suddenly relaxed and let me kiss him. I smiled at him and Barry regarded me for a moment, searching my face for something.

Whatever it was, he must have found it, because suddenly I saw the glint of a smile in his eyes and then his arms encircled my neck in an awkward hug. I kissed his cheek again and said: "Remember, next Sunday! Uncle Peter and I will be looking forward to it all the week."

Barry did not reply, but I could see a certain softening of his expression, a relaxation of the taut, wistful look. It was really the first time that day that Barry looked like the little boy of five he really was.

It was only a beginning, of course, but then there was always next Sunday and all the Sundays after.

The End.

I T'S true, then?''

"The doctor says so." Jenny Stanton's words were sharp and bitter.

Her husband came towards her, putting his hand awkwardly on her arm. "Aren't you at least a little bit pleased?"

She turned her shoulder so that he couldn't get any closer to her.

"*Pleased*?" Her voice choked on the word. She felt a wild desire to beat at his chest. Her life was as good as ruined, and Charles asked if she was *pleased*!

"When will the — when will it be?" He avoided the word "baby"; they both had. It was almost as if they were afraid of it.

"Just in time for Robin's thirteenth birthday," she commented bitterly. "A lovely birthday present for him, I must say."

Charles dropped his hand from her. There was a new hardness in his voice. "You never know . . . it might just be that."

"How can you even think . . . ?"

"I was an only child myself." He turned his back on her and went to the window.

"But thirteen years! We were going to do so much now that Robin's old enough to look after himself . . ."

Tears of helplessness rose in her throat. It was all so sudden, so bewildering. After all these years to have nappies to wash, a pram in the hall, broken nights . . . How could Charles take it so calmly?

Did he care? Did he realise what she'd have to go through? What she'd have to give up?

It had all been working out so nicely: Charles in a much better job, a little car in the garage. Robin at secondary school. She'd even started taking art classes, a dream she'd nourished from the time before she'd married.

"Did the doctor say you were to take things easy?" Charles was watching her carefully.

She felt resentful that he was still there, looking at her, seeming completely unaware of the agony of her mind.

"He said I was a fine specimen of womanhood," she replied with undisguised sarcasm. "He's sure everything will go splendidly. In fact, he seemed as pleased as Punch."

Charles shook his head, hurt in his eyes.

"That can't be bad," he said quietly.

**Her hopes, her dreams — they were all so different
from the old Mrs Stanton's —
if only her husband could see it . . .**

The New
Mrs Stanton

SHE didn't mention the baby again all week.

Robin and Charles came and went; Robin immersed in his own world of impending rugger matches and unreasonable school-masters.

Charles was quiet and withdrawn, and sometimes his eyes were quite blank when he looked at her. Yet, strangely, although it would have been unbearable a few weeks ago, she found now it left her unmoved.

In the long hours of the night, she tried to imagine her life rearranged to accommodate a small, helpless being who required attention for 24 hours a day.

The sheer bliss of a quiet house, the leisure to get out her paints and work on her latest picture — it would all be gone now.

To Jenny it had come to mean much more than just an afternoon meeting new people. She'd always known she had an eye for colour, now she was developing a sense of shape and form.

Her last two pictures had been good. Even Charles had been impressed.

"They're good," he'd said as though the admission itself amazed him. "They're jolly good."

But next Monday was the end of the present term. The classes wouldn't be starting again till winter and by that time . . .

**Complete
Story by
MAYNAH
LEWIS**

THE bus ride to the town was quite a long one and when she got to the school most of the others had already arrived.

The classroom was a vast, lofty place with an air of timelessness about it, as though a thousand students had sat here in years gone by, plying their brushes with diligent care.

Mr Dean, the teacher, seemed to have absorbed some of that timelessness. His age was impossible to judge; only his eyes were bright and hopeful.

The first five minutes were taken up by the customary ritual of half-serious inspection of one another's work. None of them expected to be in the company of a new Picasso. They were all there for the simple enjoyment of putting paint on canvas.

Today Jenny didn't take part, but sat quietly on her stool by the big window, contemplating her half-finished work.

It was a study of the room itself. A bright feathered hat stood out in a splash of crimson, a streamlined figure was suggested with an elongated stroke of the brush, there was a sense of movement in a skirt.

Before she'd even picked up her brush, Mr Dean was beside her. There was the faint but pungent smell of tobacco from his old tweed jacket.

"A little more blue in the shadows would give a greater depth," he suggested quietly.

She would miss him. She knew nothing about him except that he was patient and had the sense not to expect too much, too soon.

He was smiling down at her. "Have you enjoyed the session?"

"Oh yes!" she replied with unexpected fervour.

"I thought so." It was almost as though he was talking to himself. "You're the most promising pupil I've had for many years. You have an instinct for painting. It would be a pity if you wasted it."

He was looking at her searchingly and her lips trembled as she tried to return his smile.

"Yes," she managed to say. "Thank you."

He left her and went round the others, stopping at each easel in turn, pointing out a fault here, giving quiet encouragement there.

She worked with concentrated energy throughout the afternoon to finish the picture. It was as if she wanted to capture in it all the atmosphere of the room, to take with her a memory of all that could so easily have been hers.

Then, too soon, a bell rang and the class was over. There was the usual hubbub as paints were packed away.

The picture was still unfinished and she took a last look round the room, imprinting every detail on her memory. One day, perhaps, she would try to finish it.

"Goodbye, Mr Dean," Jenny said to him.

"See you next year, I hope, Mrs Stanton?"

Somehow she managed a smile. "Yes," she said shakily. "Perhaps."

ON the bus there was an atmosphere of sadness.

"Too bad it's the last day," one of the other women was saying.

"We mustn't break up!" It was the shrill voice of Madge Hammond. There was something approaching desperation in it and

Jenny remembered Madge was a widow, living alone in a big house.

"We'll have to take up something else . . . something to fill in the summer, just so we can keep in touch."

Jenny sat quietly while they talked about the idea and at last a gardening club was suggested . . . they all lived near enough for that.

They arranged to meet the following Monday at Madge Hammond's house to talk it over. No-one noticed that Jenny hadn't committed herself.

She called goodbye to each of them as they left the bus.

Madge Hammond was the last to leave. Jenny waved, watching her as the bus drew away. She looked such a lonely figure, waiting there to cross the road, half-empty shopping bag on her arm.

The thought came unbidden: *What would Madge give for someone to care for?* Jenny remembered her voice, shrill, almost desperate — *We'll have to take up something else . . . something to fill in the summer . . .*

And suddenly, for the first time, Jenny saw everything clearly. And she knew she'd been wrong.

She'd clung to the comfortable closed-in existence she'd built for herself, refusing to recognise the wonderful new world that was spreading out in front of her — a world that women like Madge Hammond would never know again.

As the bus passed under the dark shadows of a copse of trees she saw her own reflection in the window, the small chin, mouth a little curved, eyes wide and wistful.

But the wistfulness was no longer for herself. It was for the women who had used the painting class as an excuse to be together and who were now left high and dry, searching for a fresh outlet for their energy.

Perhaps she alone had appreciated just what Mr Dean had tried to teach them.

Try to create, he'd once said. She smiled to herself. Create! What else was she doing but that!

Every second that went by she was creating, every breath brought that creation nearer to perfection.

Perhaps it would be a girl; Charles would love a little daughter.

And Robin. He was old enough to be told now — to understand. He would adjust his life in his offhand, already half-a-man attitude.

Tomorrow she would buy some white wool and start knitting. A delicate primrose cover would look perfect, with a white pram. And tomorrow, she would finish the painting from memory and hang it in the nursery-to-be.

Some day, she promised herself, when things had settled into some sort of routine, she would go back and see Mr Dean. He'd be glad to see her. She had an idea that nothing would be changed, the easels and the stools had been there too long for that.

Suddenly she couldn't get home quickly enough. There were things to do, a setting to be prepared for her new creation.

And, above all, there was the urgent need to see the light put back into the depth of Charles's eyes.

The End.

DICK-DICK The Hen That Was One Of The Family

She reigned supreme in a house with three dogs, two cats and four doting humans.

DURING the war we kept about a dozen hens in a run in our garden. Dick-Dick was one of a batch of five-month-old pullets.

We used to let them meander about the lawn, and chase them back into their run when twilight came.

At that time, with invasion a strong possibility, the Army had erected a six-foot-deep barbed-wire entanglement over part of our lawn.

This was the joy of Dick-Dick's life.

As soon as David, my husband, tried to get the hens back into their run in the evenings she would make a dash for the middle of the barbed wire.

She would then play hide-and-seek with him for hours.

One evening, in the middle of this performance, David picked up a small lump of earth and threw it at her. He meant it to land behind her and scare her into the run.

It hit her leg and broke it.

Quite upset, David braved the barbed wire and brought the injured bird into the house.

We all crowded round, stroking the frightened and indignant little hen, and wondered what to do.

David rang a farmer friend for advice. When he came off the phone he looked upset. "He says, wring her neck."

"Oh, no!" a horrified cry went up from the girls and me.

"I wouldn't dream of killing her," he muttered grimly. "I injured her so I'll mend her — I *am* a doctor after all."

He made her a little splint of stiffened cardboard — not wood, in case it should chafe her, and bandaged it firmly, despite her outraged squawkings.

We gave her a large cardboard box filled with straw and put it in our stone-floored scullery.

Here she reigned supreme. The box was deep enough for her to feel safe and enclosed, but not too deep to prevent her from viewing our daily comings and goings.

A T that time we had three dogs and two cats, and they all reacted differently to the new addition to the family.

Judy, a large black Labrador-type mongrel, with generous and affectionate heart, lolloped up to the box and prepared to give Dick-Dick the sloshing lick with which she welcomed all newcomers.

Dick-Dick, startled by this enthusiastic black apparition, ruffled her feathers and squawked fiercely. Judy had to make do with an experimental sniff and a tail-wag.

Evidently mollified, Dick-Dick settled back into her box to accept her welcome.

The other two dogs, advancing suspiciously with raised hackles, took their cue from Judy, and an understanding was established.

We'd been worried about how the cats would react, but Dick-Dick's dignified calm seemed to unnerve them.

The younger cat took one look, spat viciously, and retreated in disorder. Micky, the older one, who had been with us since kittenhood, plodded pompously up to the box, held Dick-Dick's bright gaze for a moment with his own amber eyes then, with a twitch of his tail, stalked away and sulked in his box for the next hour.

At first, of course, we had to lift Dick-Dick out on to the floor and remove the rest of the "animal kingdom," while she had her meals.

Fairly soon, though, she was able to hop out of her box and limp around by herself.

The dogs and cats grew accustomed to her, and accepted her as one of the family. The only time they showed any resentment was when Dick-Dick decided their food looked more appetising than her own and tried to sample some of it.

After a couple of weeks David took the splint off her leg, and we all congratulated him on a very neat piece of work. Very soon she didn't limp at all, and ultimately we couldn't even tell which leg had been broken.

When we judged she was quite recovered we put her back in the run with the other hens. This turned out to be a big mistake — they all attacked her.

by EVELYN JOYCE

We realised then that Dick-Dick, having lived with humans for so long, was now unacceptable to her own kind. So back she went into her box in the scullery, with the run of the garden as consolation for her ostracism.

She seemed happy enough with her quarters, but with the unpredictability of her kind, she decided to lay in the coal-hole behind the scullery.

So we moved her box in there, and there she slept till the end of her days.

S HE became more and more tame, and as time went by she began to recognise her name, and would come when called.

In the summer we would leave the dining-room window open at the bottom, and at meal-times Dick-Dick would jump in at the window with a little "Crrrk," and wander round, pecking up any crumbs.

After lunch she would hop out again and potter about the garden till twilight, when she would come stalking up the path and put herself to bed.

Sometimes at night, not sure whether she was in or not, I would put my head into the dark coal-hole and say, "Are you there, Dick-Dick?" and would always be answered by a sleepy "Crrrk."

The children, of course, adored her, and showed this in all sorts of ways. I remember one Christmas when David and I were summoned upstairs to the nursery to see a home-made Nativity scene which they had made.

A cardboard box did duty for a crib. Round it were propped teddy bears and dolls arrayed in dusters and odd bits of cloth representing the Wise Men. In the crib sat Dick-Dick, white, comfortable and uncomplaining.

DURING the seven years of her life all our friends said we were mad.

"You ought to put her in the pot. Times are hard," they said. "A good old boiling fowl . . ."

"You don't eat your *friends*," the children used to say indignantly. We couldn't have agreed more.

One day when she was seven years old she fell ill. We nursed her devotedly and hopefully, but to no avail.

She was buried with sorrow and honours under the lilacs beside old Mick, who had received her with such proud indifference, but who learned to love her as much as we all did.

Dear Dick-Dick. Before we buried her I removed the blue ring which she had worn round her leg, and I have it still, in memory of a friend and part of our family.

None of us will ever forget her.

The End.

Blame It On The Little People

Well, to be truthful, there were no "little people" seen in that crazy corner of Ireland . . . but when you think of all the wondrous things that happened that day — it makes you think.

IT is generally accepted that the trouble between Bridget Bell and Michael Costigan didn't really begin until the day Bridget's uncle and guardian, Liam Bell, decided to sell his omnibus.

It was a square, dumpy bus, with bulging sides, worn leather seats, a door that closed like a concertina, and a raucous klaxon horn.

One day, in the middle of an Irish summer, Uncle Liam stood looking at the bus and stroking his chin thoughtfully.

He called his niece from the store, which she helped him run.

"Bridget," he said, "I'm thinking I'll sell the old girl. The store is making enough money now to support us both. So even if you won't accept Michael

Costigan's proposal of marriage it doesn't really matter."

Bridget's eyes flashed, and she tossed her dark hair.

"Michael Costigan is a brute," she said, keeping her head high by watching a linnet, perched in a blackthorn bush.

"He thinks he can dangle his good looks and his legacy in front of a girl like — like a carrot before a donkey. For all I care," she finished, "Michael Costigan can take a jump in the ocean."

The fact that Bridget meant what she said was proved two days later when Michael Costigan came into the store.

"Bridget," he said, "you look a picture. I want to see your Uncle Liam about buying the bus."

He leaned on the counter and gazed at her with clear blue eyes. "I've been thinking about it. It'll sort of cement relations a bit when we get married."

"Michael Costigan," Bridget said, "I wouldn't marry you if you were the last man this side of the Atlantic. And as for this other business, I have a feeling you'll be unlucky there, too."

That evening when she was spooning him a plateful of his favourite Irish stew, Bridget announced to Uncle Liam that she had found him a customer for the bus.

The taste of the stew was spoiled and Uncle Liam choked. "Joe Maclauchlan! But I'm selling to Michael Costigan. We shook hands on it. It's irrevocable."

"It's nothing of the sort," Bridget snapped. She spooned out more stew and held it under Uncle Liam's nose. "If Michael Costigan buys your bus," she said, "it's the last you'll be tasting."

Uncle Liam groaned. "Bridget, you wouldn't. Not to your old Uncle Liam."

Complete Story by
DEREK TAYLOR

Bridget scraped out the saucepan. "If Michael Costigan buys your bus, I'll be off to the city so fast you won't see me."

Uncle Liam looked into her eyes and he didn't doubt her word. He just wondered what he was going to tell Michael Costigan . . .

The change of ownership of the old blue boneshaker was smoothly accomplished and for a few weeks all went well.

Then suddenly, one day, there was competition. It came in the shape of a brand-new, gleaming bright, 32-seater, standing in the square.

It was painted a patriotic emerald green. And there at the wheel sat Michael Costigan.

"A little competition never hurt anyone," he said to Bridget. "And besides, think how handy it'll be when we get married to carry the guests from the church to Macready's place for the wedding party."

Bridget's cheeks flushed pink and she stamped her foot. "You're a brute, Michael Costigan — a bragging, conceited, over-confident brute — and I hate you."

She left then to think about the problem, and a few days later she went to see Joe Maclauchlan.

"It's like a race now," he told Bridget, "from one stop to the next, and he has the edge on me. I didn't make enough today to pay for the petrol."

When Bridget smiled, Joe looked puzzled.

"It's Darrydown market the day after tomorrow," she said. "Now just you close that bonnet and listen to me.

NEXT morning the news was out. After a heated argument down at Macready's place Joe Maclauchlan had challenged Michael Costigan to an omnibus race.

They were to start off together for Darrydown market and see who was first to the town hall.

By a gentleman's agreement no passengers or livestock were to be left standing at the stops. And the winner was to be recognised without argument as the sole omnibus proprietor in Ballykee.

"Sole omnibus proprietor in Ballykee, Bridget," Michael Costigan said, when he came into the store. "It's something I've always fancied — a nice, secure future to offer a wife. We'll get married straight after, if it suits you."

Bridget whisked bacon across the slicer. "One of these days, Michael Costigan, you'll learn a little humility."

For once she wasn't angry, and noticing this Michael Costigan left the store looking a little more thoughtful than he usually did.

Uncle Liam had also overheard the conversation.

"Humility," he muttered. "Now how do you make a man like Michael Costigan feel humility?"

Next day the half of the population that wasn't actually in one or the other of the buses turned out to see the start.

There were, as everyone knew, eight pick-ups into Darrydown on market day. So it looked very much as if the bus that reached the first group of passengers first would be the eventual winner.

The driver could work it alternately then, so that his rival was left with the last group to pick up while he himself got his nose in front.

"It'll be a dawdle." Michael Costigan grinned to Bridget. "If you want to come along we can buy the ring in Darrydown this very day."

"I'm travelling with Uncle Liam," she answered coolly. "And we'll be in Joe Maclauchlan's bus."

Soon after this, to a roar that could be heard in Castleblarney, the two buses shot away. And even before they were out of sight of the village it was the emerald green nose of Michael Costigan's bus that was showing in front.

Ten minutes later, when he drew up at the first group of passengers with the old blue boneshaker half a mile behind, his supporters were jubilant. And when, while they were still loading up, Joe Maclauchlan flashed by with his klaxon hooting they all cheered him.

"Have no fear," Michael shouted back to his passengers, "we'll be passing him again in five minutes when he stops at the Hennessy place."

At the Hennessy place the positions were indeed reversed. And now other names sprang to excited lips. After the Hennessys came the Donovans, Kellys, Macmahons, Shaws, Mulligans, and last of all the Skeffingtons.

Bridget and Uncle Liam were sitting side by side in Maclauchlan's bus watching Joe feverishly loading Kelly's chicks on board when Michael Costigan flashed by, his horn hooting derisively.

Uncle Liam sighed. "Well, Bridget," he said, "it looks like the end of the road for this old girl. 'Tis a pity, but I cannot see us beating Michael Costigan now."

The words were sad words and the old bus seemed to shudder and snort in agreement. Yet strangely in Uncle Liam's voice Bridget thought she could detect a note of faint amusement.

They rattled on again and passed Costigan at the Macmahons.

"Now we've got him." Bridget laughed.

Uncle Liam glanced at her sharply. But in the excitement of being overtaken while they manoeuvred Brendan Shaw's ninety-two-year-old mother aboard he forgot about it.

SAD to say, despondency now set in among Joe Maclauchlan's supporters. They could see the Costigan bus ahead flying down the hill and round the bend to where it would make its last pick-up at the Mulligans'.

They would pass it all right, but would then be obliged to stop at the Skeffingtons'.

"Ah, an' we've had it — and that is certain," Uncle Liam said, shaking his head and taking out his pipe. "That Michael Costigan has done it, just as he said he would."

But when they got round that self-same bend themselves and saw the scene confronting them, there was an amazed buzz of excitement and then a great shouting from the Maclauchlan bus.

"Sure, an' it seems Michael has a bit of trouble there," Uncle Liam remarked, puffing at his old briar. "Quite a bit of trouble by the look of things."

The cause of the sudden jubilation in the Maclauchlan bus was on account of about a dozen of Tim Mulligan's piglets, which seemed somehow to have escaped in the process of being loaded aboard.

While Tim's great layabout son, Shamus, stood watching, Michael Costigan himself, with his cap falling off the back of his head, chased the piglets all over the county.

"It serves him right," said Bridget with a smile. "It looks as if he'll not get to Darrydown market today, let alone this morning."

The prophecy, indeed, turned out to be more or less correct. It was over an hour later, when, to a resounding cheer from the Maclauchlan supporters, a red-faced Michael Costigan coaxed his bus into the town hall square.

The surprising thing was that Michael himself seemed mightily pleased. Humiliated on the surface, to be sure, but underneath — well, that was a different story.

A COUPLE of days later Michael Costigan walked into Uncle Liam's store. "Bridget, you look a picture," he said with the braggart gone from him. "It's in humility I come, begging your forgiveness for all I've ever said and done that's made you unhappy."

Bridget continued cutting cheese and weighed it on the scales. "If your words are sincere you may continue, Michael Costigan. But one hint of boasting an I'll not listen."

"Don't run out on me," Michael began, and he took Bridget's hand in his, as if to prevent it. "What I meant was, will you consider taking me as your husband, your lawful wedded, for richer or poorer?

"And if it's not taking too much for granted I'd like you to know I've bought a little farm out Fairtown way that'll suit us just fine."

Bridget smiled. "Ah, Michael Costigan. That's all I've been waiting to hear you say these past twelve months. I knew you could do it properly if only you tried hard enough."

When Michael lifted her over the counter she was smiling to herself. The fiver she'd slipped Shamus Mulligan to let the piglets loose had been money well spent.

At the same time, Michael Costigan, too, was congratulating himself along similar lines. The five quid he'd slipped Shamus Mulligan to put on the act with the pigs was just about the best investment he'd ever made.

He wouldn't stay humble for ever, he decided, but certainly long enough to get Bridget Bell to the altar.

Unbeknown to either of them, Uncle Liam was watching. Sticking her thumbs in his braces, he emitted a proud sigh.

Neither of 'em will ever know, he thought, that it cost me five quid to young Shamus Mulligan to bring about this little scene.

The wedding was in the autumn. Michael Costigan, in the meantime, sold his bus to Joe Maclauchlan on the never-never. The old boneshaker was relegated to Donovan's field, where it later did good service as a hen coop.

Shamus Mulligan used his windfall towards buying a passage to England and was never heard of again.

But in Ballykee they still talk about the great omnibus race to this very day . . .

The End.

Complete Story by SUSAN SALLIS

THE
Prisoner

She herself held the key for her escape back to those who loved and needed her. If she could find the courage to use it . . .

IT had been very hot all day. And all day Charlotte lay baking in the sun, her pale shoulders oiled, her fingers lazily sifting the scorching sand.

Around her, children dug and quarrelled and whined for ice-cream and donkey rides, but she scarcely heard them as she drifted in her own world.

After dinner that evening she sat in the hotel lounge discussing the English weather with her dining companion. It was the most unpredictable thing in the world, they agreed, and the sudden drop in the evening temperature was ample proof of the statement.

Charlotte had planned a half-hour stroll along the deserted, rocky headland, then an early night, just as she had promised Ron. Now, suddenly, she wanted noise and lights and, above all, people!

Her dinner neighbour was hanging on to the weather conversation too long. She was older than Charlotte, sparse, almost starved, over-eager to strike up a friendship.

"You here alone, too?" she asked.

Charlotte was startled into an unwary nod. She had been completely absorbed in the unexpected excitement of the flickering sheet lightning in the purple sky outside.

"It's a lonely business, isn't it?" Once again the woman gave and asked for sympathy.

Charlotte laughed and glanced around the crowded dining-room.

Her companion flushed a little.

"Well, you know what I mean. Perhaps we could get together occasionally? There are some wonderful walks . . ."

Charlotte sipped her coffee cautiously and watched the *Fun Pier* sign through the window as it flashed on and off like a pulse beat. What was it Ron had said? "Get as much sun as you can. Make friends. Above all, enjoy yourself."

She finished her coffee in a gulp and pushed back her chair.

"Yes, we must do that," she said. "Perhaps tomorrow —"

She felt mean as she went upstairs to her room for a cardigan. The little woman had looked like a crumpled napkin, left there alone at the table. But Ron had told her to enjoy herself and the neon lights were beckoning.

Once outside, the sense of time running away abated for a while. She wandered along the front, sliding

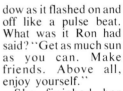

her fingers on the rail where she could, moving aside for the endless, entwined couples.

Against the lightning the clouds were piled close to the sea in fantastic gondola shapes, and a little breeze lifted her hair and blew cold on her forehead.

She tied the sleeves of her cardigan in a loose knot around her neck and dug her hands deep into the patch pockets of her navy skirt.

She was conscious of a tense excitement. As if something was going to happen. Perhaps it was the storm, the long warning it was giving, the pressure of the heat all around.

Somehow she felt at one with the crowds around the pier, in a way she hadn't felt during the long, hot afternoon on the beach.

She eyed them in the neon-lit darkness, absorbed and interested.

The cockle stalls were doing a roaring trade. After a day of iced drinks and cucumber sandwiches, appetites were tickled by the salty cockles. The stall-holders plied their trade busily, one eye on the ominous sky.

Next to them were the toffee apple and candy-floss booths. Then the turnstile and the little train that took you right to the end of the pier where the big wheel turned endlessly and the Dodgem cars chased each other in time to the music.

Charlotte took her place on the train behind a fat woman in a bright yellow sundress.

"Mind my blisters, love!"

Charlotte found it hard to restrain the laughter that bubbled in her throat as the woman's husband cowered into the corner away from the starched yellow gingham. Harder still not to join in the raucous singing from the next coach.

The open coaches swayed slowly down the length of the pier, and at last the prickly air blew cool on hot faces.

Charlotte ran her fingers through her hair and allowed herself to think of Ron and Caro . . . and, just for a second, of Dilly. Dilly, whose hair was like spun gold. Dilly, whose sweet little ways had captured every heart. Dilly — the reason for her being here.

But she mustn't think of Dilly! She must think of other things from now on.

She wondered what Ron would tell Caro, because Caro would ask endlessly.

Ron would be quite simple and straightforward as usual. He would say gently, "The doctor says Mummy must have a holiday," and there would be no bitterness anywhere.

She was the only one who felt bitterness, it seemed. But not now. She had escaped from that now.

The fat woman nudged her. "You all right, ducky? Feeling the heat?"

Charlotte shook her head and smiled her wide, unexpected smile. "I'm happy," she said simply.

"Well, I suppose we all are, ducky, after a year's hard saving for one week down here!" The yellow dress was eased carefully over one red shoulder. "Though what with blisters and them bawling kids in the next coach, you got to keep reminding yourself of it, I dare say!"

Charlotte let the laughter bubble from her throat, and the woman joined her, echoed by her small husband. The boys in front stopped singing and glanced round at the adults. They all laughed together.

She was swept across to the Dodgem cars with them, still laughing, and squashed into the driver's seat next to the yellow dress.

They tore round the track, sparks flashing, the hot, oily air vibrating with rock 'n' roll music.

Then the husband took Charlotte's place. She tucked him in carefully and said goodbye.

"It's been lovely. To be a human being again with other human beings."

The fat woman screamed with delight and turned her face as they plunged away. "You're a right one — you are!"

A WAY from the noise for a moment the air was no clearer. Charlotte could feel it in her lungs, heavy and warm and sweet.

Lightning still flickered in the sky, but it was too dark to see the purple gondolas any more.

People sat around like fish, mopping their faces, eating chips.

She sat with them for a while, her cardigan in her lap, her loose white sandals on the seat in front. She tried to relax, regulating her breathing, forcing her legs to feel heavy, but a little pulse in her neck leapt and her hands tightened on her navy skirt.

She got up and went over to the big wheel.

The man who took her money was big, with dark curly hair growing into a thick neck. His blue eyes looked at her without interest.

"On your own, love? Same price for one as for two."

She gave him some money and watched his hands as he fumbled for change. They were brown and smudged with oil and dirt, but they were like hers — square and blunt-fingered.

He put his hand under her elbow and helped her into the shallow seat and fastened the safety bar across her lap.

All the time she couldn't take her eyes off the hard-knotted hands.

"Feeling queer, love?" Like the woman in the yellow dress, he was suddenly concerned, the blue eyes no longer impersonal.

It was strange that, tonight, surrounded by people she'd never seen before, she felt this contact with them. A peculiar closeness that for the past few months she hadn't even felt with her family.

Their fleeting compassion was no longer a thing to be brushed aside with angry impatience. It could be returned, doubled and trebled.

"Our hands are the same shape," she said suddenly, without thought. "Workaday hands, my father called them."

The man looked at his hands as if he had never seen them before, and then glanced at her doubtfully. She had a terrible fear that his face would shut down against her.

Instead, the blue eyes sparkled and he cocked his head interestedly. "Well, now, that's something I'd never have given a thought! My, but you are an interestin' one, aren't you?"

He glanced round at the queue. "Give us a few minutes and I'll join you!"

He tipped her float so that it rocked wildly and pulled the lever with a sickening wrench, sending her up a few feet while he loaded the next float.

She sat gasping and looking out to sea. He hadn't thought — oh, surely he hadn't thought —!

She leaned cautiously over the side and he laughed up at her and gave her a cheery wave.

Like a little girl she stifled her own giggles in her handkerchief. If only Ron knew. And, of course, she could tell him. At last there would be something to talk about.

He would laugh — if she could make the man laugh, she could make Ron laugh again. And there was the woman in the yellow sundress with the blisters — Ron would enjoy that, too.

The wheel bore her quickly upwards now. All the floats were full, and the dark sea swept away from her dizzily.

Six times they went round before the brake ground on and the reloading began all over again. Charlotte waited for her turn to come round.

She stuffed her handkerchief into her pocket and slipped her arms into the sleeves of her cardigan. She spread her left hand on the safety bar so that her wedding ring was obvious.

The big man worked busily, taking money, helping passengers on and off, releasing the brake and clamping it on again.

But as Charlotte's float swung on to the platform he signalled to somebody in the crowd, and was sitting beside her, the safety bar in place, before she could move.

"This one's on me, love," he said grandly, leaning back against the red plush. "Old Gramps'll take over for a couple of spins."

The float tipped at an uncomfortable angle under his weight. Charlotte tried to sit up.

"But all those people —"

"They'll soon be gone, love. This storm won't hold off much longer."

He sat up suddenly to shout some instructions to Old Gramps, and they soared up to the level of the fortune-teller's roof.

"Come on now, sit back and relax!"

CALLING — CARD?

I was listening to a friend (aged 80) phoning an order to a big store. She addressed the person on the other end of the line as "young man."

"How do you know he's young?" I enquired.

"I don't," she replied, "but if he's young he thinks I'm an old battleaxe and he'd better hop to it. If he's older he's so flattered that he's ready to eat out of my hand! Either way I get good service."

SHARE AND SHARE . . .

A white-haired old man was tenderly guiding a wheelchair in which his wife sat. Every now and then they exchanged affectionate smiles.

Just as they drew level with me, I heard him say, "My turn now, dear."

To my amazement the old lady got out of the chair with unexpected agility. Her husband took her place, and they went on their way — with her pushing!

She leaned back and found herself rubbing shoulders with him. "Really, I should get off. I didn't mean —"

He grinned down at her and she could see he didn't care what she had meant.

"You felt a bit mad, eh, love? And you're regretting it now?" His voice held no reproof, but she felt her cheeks go hot.

"D'you know what to blame it on? The storm. There's nothing in this world you can't blame on the weather!"

She felt her mouth stretch into a grin. They jerked up again unsteadily and she jogged against him. He threw his arm round her shoulders.

"I'm married," she protested on a high, bleating note as the wind came in from the sea and took her breath away.

"Me, too!" She could feel his shoulder shaking with laughter. "Smashing, isn't it — marriage, I mean?"

She looked into the night and thought about Ron, and nodded.

They started to move smoothly aand swiftly now, soaring up and gliding down in a reassuring rhythm.

HE picked up her hand and turned it over to look at the palm. "Workaday hand? Bit white and smooth for a name like that."

She looked down at her hand again. It did look very white against his big brown one.

"I've been in hospital a long time."

"Recuperatin', eh? Lots comes down here for that. Air like wine down here."

"Yes." She looked into his dark face warily. "I was in a mental hospital."

His shoulder shook again.

"I knew you was bonkers the minute I saw you."

There was no withdrawal, no embarrassment, no rush of sympathy. He didn't care where she had come from or where she might be going. She was just a girl to laugh with and leave in five minutes.

He grasped her arm as they swung upwards again.

"Look at that sky, love! Ever see anything like that before?"

She stared with him. The lightning fidgeted around the edge of the sea. The clouds moved clumsily, heavily, almost on top of the pier. People glanced up at them, half-frightened, edging closer into the packed crowd.

"Not for a long time," she whispered. "I've been — away —"

They swooped over the top of the circle and down again. She heard his lungs fill with a mighty gasp.

"Good to be on this thing tonight. You can't hardly breathe . . . Marvellous, isn't it, girl, up here on top of the world?

"Not too long, mind. You don't want to get away from things too long, I reckon. On the wheel you're up there long enough to see it all, like you was on a cloud. Then down you goes again —"

The float tore on its way.

Charlotte said breathlessly, "I feel just like that tonight. It's so good to be in the world again instead of on the outside."

She wanted to tell him about Dilly and her parents and how she had tried to go back in time and find them again. But she had told others, and they had been gentle, too gentle, and said kindly, "It will get better."

The big man laughed again, his head thrown back. There were a myriad criss-crossed lines in his skin.

"I knew it. When you made that crazy remark about my hands I knew just how you felt."

He pointed a blunt finger at the crowds below. "Most days you don't see 'em then suddenly they're all there, alive and breathin' just like you!"

"And they don't have to be alive to be there!" She was blazing with excitement now. "They can be in you — and in other people, too. The ones that have gone."

Her voice shook for a moment, then she said, "It gets so that you can love everyone, because they've all got something that goes on for ever, even after death."

" 'Ere, take it easy, love." He took her hand and held it tightly in his warm grasp. "You don't have to go into it too deep, y'know. That's something you just feel."

The float rocked as the wheel began to slow. Charlotte looked down at the clasped hands and then out to the endless sea.

She remembered the doctors at home who had repeated, sickeningly, "Try to face reality, my dear," and she had thought reality was Dilly's death.

"Thank you," she said slowly. "My father always said that people with the same sort of hands thought the same sort of things."

"Ay." He looked up critically at the fretwork of steel above their heads. "It isn't everyone who appreciates the big wheel."

They ground to a stop on the wooden platform and he helped her out.

"Stick around. The lightning'll scare away the crowds pretty soon and you can have a free ride."

But she wanted to go now and be by herself to look at this new gift.

BEFORE she reached the hotel it began to rain — huge drops that exploded on her hot face. She watched the front empty of its strolling couples and began to run herself, smiling at the flurrying skirts and shrieks of dismay.

The lightning stopped its restless darting and lit up the sea in one mighty flash. The thunder cracked and shook the cockle stalls angrily.

The shelters were full to bursting, and people dived for passing buses, heads down, heels kicking up splashes of water in the road.

Charlotte was wet to the skin by the time she reached the hotel lobby. She shook herself like a puppy and pushed her soaking hair behind her ears.

The little Italian waitress, skimming upstairs with a tray of coffee cups, paused sympathetically.

"You have coffee in the television lounge?" she suggested.

Charlotte thought about it. "Yes, please. But I must change first and make a telephone call."

Her neighbour from the dinner table hovered uncertainly at the head of the stairs. Charlotte had a feeling she had been there all evening.

"Oh, you are wet," she said self-consciously.

Charlotte laughed, feeling irritation and caution melt away.

"I'm going to get dry and then have some coffee and watch the television. Won't you join me?"

"Yes, I'd like that." The anxious face smiled. Charlotte turned at her bedroom door and looked into her eyes.

"Please don't mind if I'm — abrupt." The door handle turned in her hand. "Sometimes I have to get away. My little girl died, and I've been ill."

There was a small silence that had nothing to do with embarrassment. Then the older woman said quietly, "I was like that when my mother died. It gets better."

"Yes, it gets better," Charlotte whispered humbly. She smiled at the woman.

IN her bedroom she towelled her hair and changed into a dress and cardigan. Then she sat on the edge of the bed and picked up her telephone.

The operator must have left a switch on, for she could hear the call on its way to Ron.

When she heard his voice she nearly cried, because it was so long since she had really heard it. They had lived together as strangers for almost eight months.

She said straightaway, without any greeting, "Darling, it's all right now. I'm not alone any more."

There was a pause while he registered her tone and weighed the worth of her words. Then he said slowly, "You've never been alone, Charlotte. You just thought you were."

"I know. Darling, I'm sorry. Have I — have I done too much damage?"

"Don't be silly." He told her how much he loved her and what Caro had had for tea. Then he said, "Sweetheart, do you mean it — I mean, what happened?"

Her heart ached for the caution in his voice. She laughed gaily. "A storm happened. Can you hear it?"

She held the receiver towards the window where the rain lashed relentlessly. "Everybody's been hurrying to enjoy themselves before it broke. I was there, with them. We were almost scared by it, so we forgot we were strangers and talked and laughed. Together."

"I know."

There was so much warmth and sympathy around me all the time, she thought wonderingly, and I couldn't see it.

"I'll ring you tomorrow," she cried. "A hug for Caro . . ."

The End.

COME ONE, COME ALL

One Sunday morning when I was out with my corgi dog, I paused to glance in through the open west door of a small church. A service was in progress.

I was seen by the verger, who indicated that I could go in. I pointed to my dog, but still he beckoned me in. Warily we joined him in the back pew. He handed me a hymn book.

"We've got *four* dogs in church this morning," he whispered proudly.

HOOKED LINE AND SINKER

T O the vast army of fanatical
fishers — excuse me, anglers!
— fishing is a very serious
business, indeed.

When I married one of this curious
breed, however, I went along strictly
for the laughs — and, believe me,
there are plenty.

When I first met my husband it was
the close season which, he assured
me, has nothing whatever to do with
the shops being closed. It's a period
during which the many varieties of
fish found in lakes and rivers are
breeding, and must be left alone to
get on with it in peace. Any angler
caught violating this rule is severely
fined.

Consequently, the first time I ever
held a rod and reel it was on a tiny
wooden pier surrounded by hordes of
sea anglers.

Suddenly, my rod bent double. For
what seemed like hours I struggled
valiantly with the mighty force at the
other end. Eventually, flushed with
triumph and under the envious gaze
of all the other anglers, I pulled from
the sea — an old fishing rod
complete with heavy reel and half a
ton of seaweed on the end of it!

Since that unhappy day I have
spent countless hours at lakes and

**When her husband went
fishing, Olive Moody
went along, too,
strictly for laughs. But
she found that more often
than not, the laughs
were on her.**

rivers throughout the country, in fine
weather and foul — mostly foul.

The marvellous thing about fishing
is that there's absolutely no need to
dress up for it. In fact, I often think
there's a kind of rivalry among
anglers as to who can look the most
outrageous!

It's quite commonplace to see
men, who during the week wear
sober and dignified attire, sporting
boaters trimmed with old ties,
sou'westers — in blazing sunshine —
woolly tea-cosy type hats, and, of
course, the favourite battered tweed
pudding-basins — my husband's
favourite!

120

THERE'S a lot of good fishing to be had in gravel pits and we were visiting a particularly deep one when I bent to wash my hands, lost my balance and fell in with a terrific splash.

My dachshund weighed up the situation in a flash, wagged her tail, and promptly jumped in beside me. I had the job of hauling her, as well as myself, up the steep and slippery bank.

Drenched with mud, water and self-pity, I squelched round to my husband, who was fishing a few yards away, hoping for a few sympathetic words.

All I heard as I drew near was: "There must be a jolly big one in there — you should have heard him splash!"

LIKE every angler worth his salt, I have a classic one-that-got-away story. Only mine was achieved without even a rod.

I was wandering along the river bank in my usual idle fashion with the landing net in my hands when I saw a simply enormous fish lying on top of the water, basking in the sunshine.

Gently easing the net under him, I scooped him up, nearly breaking my arm in the process.

Just as I called out triumphantly: "Look what I've got!" the silly thing leapt about ten yards in the air and plopped back into the river.

As it happened, it was lucky for me that it did its high-diving act, because it was a salmon — and I should probably have had to pay a hefty fine for poaching.

Of all the types of fish there are, most anglers have a particular favourite, and my husband's is tench.

We've chased this elusive fish around the waters of Britain, occasionally, amidst great rejoicing, catching one or two.

Tench are sometimes called the doctor fish and I used to fondly imagine them with little stethoscopes slung round their gills and tiny black bag tucked under their fins, swimming earnestly about visiting their sick patients.

The prosaic, but still quite interesting, explanation is that if a fish is feeling a bit green about the gills he only has to rub himself against a tench and he feels better again. Sweet, isn't it?

WHEN our son was born the first thing his father did, naturally, was to buy him a miniature rod and reel. He started fishing last summer, aged three, in a salt-water lake with a small net and a jam-jar, in the time-honoured way of all little boys.

His first catch was a repulsive-looking jelly fish and, with a horrified expression, he flung it and the net into the water, proclaiming loudly: "I think fishing's silly." I can see a tough fight ahead!

Quite seriously, though, if your husband is an angler go along with him. Enjoy the fresh air, the peace and quiet — and a good laugh!

If you're not married go along anyway. It's a very good way to judge a man's character. If he enjoys sitting all day without a bite and then catches a beauty only to return it to the water, he must be a good type!

Just think of all that patience, determination to succeed, not to mention the kindness of heart.

A word of warning, though — remember not to catch more fish than he does, or that heart may not feel so kind any more!

After the day's fishing when everyone gathers at the nearest pub to swop fishy tales, hold your hands just a modest few inches apart, and when someone remarks: "That was a small one," reply nonchalantly: "Oh, that was just the space between his eyes!" □

Wouldn't you know it with a man like Emlyn. There he was, in the land of his fathers, back among his own people again . . . and feeling like a fish out of water

R ESOLUTEL Emlyn Jenk gripped his travell bag and stepped do from the two-carri train on to the t platform. At t barrier, the ticl collector stared at h

A solitary taxi wai on the rank. As Em opened the door, driver gave him a lo knowing look recognition.

"Mrs Thoma place, is it?" the dri said, starting engine.

For a moment Em was irritated. H forgotten how eve body knew everybe else's busine hereabouts.

"That's right," said resignedly, "P Thomas's place."

As they dro through the valley, driver threw curio sidelong glanc towards him. "Up Newcastle, aren't y mun?"

"No, Durham."

The driver nod but didn't lo impressed.

"You've come ho for the Press christening. I suppo . . . Used to be frien with Megan at time, didn't y mun?"

Complete Story by MALCOLM WILLIAMS

122

The Prodigal's Return

"You seem very well formed," Emlyn owled.

He scowled out at the phalt sky, the over-ad pit buckets, the et slate roofs, the eat black pyramids of ag. Nothing had anged. Already he as beginning to regret e trip back here.

NEXT morning, Emlyn sat in the ullery watching his unt Anna making ead.

As far back as he uld remember, this ual had been one of e great pleasures of ving in this house. It ok him right back to ildhood, made him ace again the little boy ho'd lost his parents a plane crash, the ghtened child whose e had been pieced gether again by his nt's care.

"Your telegram gave e quite a jolt, mlyn." She peered to the oven and slid t another loaf with a wel. "I mean, after ur years away . . . I ought something ust be wrong."

"I got a letter from egan inviting me to e christening," he plied.

His aunt faced him, wiping toil-grooved hands on her pinafore. "It might have been wiser not to come, Emlyn. Megan was very fond of you once, you know."

"I remember. But I went away and she married Tregelles."

"If you hadn't gone away she would have married you."

"Megan would never have left the valley . . ."

"There's nothing wrong with this valley, Emlyn," she said, a hint of sadness in her voice.

Emlyn shook his head. "There was never any future here."

His aunt fiddled with a spare twist of dough on the table. "Trouble always was with you, Emlyn, you were too superior. Going away to an English college and all. If you'd been content, like Tregelles now, you'd be settled. You've lost touch with your home the same way you lost Megan."

"It's not as simple as that, Aunt Anna," he said. "Megan preferred Tregelles — and a job up in the forestry. I wanted to get on . . ."

"Tregelles got on! He's a foreman now, drives a Land-Rover. They've got a fine baby, too. You'll only cause upset by going to see them."

"Megan invited me."

She sighed. "Does Tregelles know?"

"He *is* her husband . . ." Emlyn stood up. "I think it's time I went along to say hello and see what the christening arrangements are."

HE felt conspicuous strolling up Sebastopol Street. Some neighbours nodded at him, a few grunted formal Welsh greetings, several squinted out from behind potted ferns in windows.

But everyone gave him that uneasy look that said: *See how these young people get once they've left the valley!*

Emlyn bowed his head into the drizzle, stepped off the pavement to avoid a gang of children having pram races down the hill.

As he stepped back to regain his bearings he heard a voice calling his name. The Rev. Thomas Evans was crossing the road towards him.

"Emlyn, my boy, you've been away too long," he said warmly, shaking Emlyn's hand. "Working like mad for your doctorate, I suppose . . . What's it to be then? The law? A don?"

123

The minister smiled but there was censure in his eyes. Emlyn smiled politely, talked shop, but even the minister was on the defensive. "I hear you're going to the christening tomorrow. Seen the baby yet?"

"Er, no, I'm calling there later . . . I'm out on an errand . . . Yes, it's a long way to come . . . nice seeing you again . . ."

Emlyn walked on. He needed breathing space. Four years was a long time, and up in Durham Megan and the young love they'd shared had all belonged to the past. But here it was easy to slip back into old ways.

He made his way via Chapel Road up the short climb of mountain to the forestry edge.

I must be mad coming back here, he scolded himself. But the wind was sweet with pine and the rain pecked gently at the trees. He lit a cigarette and watched a hawk sail high above the forestry.

His face relaxed as he recalled something of the old days when his father had taken him for walks through the forestry to spot jays and foxes. Sometimes they'd followed the mountain stream and seen trout and otters. That had been a warm, carefree time, full of love and meaning . . .

Voices interrupted his brief reverie. Two people were coming towards him along the forestry path.

Emlyn didn't recognise the girl, but he knew the tall man beside her flicking at fern tops with a freshly-cut walking stick.

"So you're back then," Tregelles said, not exactly cold, but gruff. "We got your telegram. Seen our Megan yet?"

Instinctively, Emlyn pinched out his cigarette. "Not yet."

Tregelles turned to the girl beside him. "This is Gweno — from over the mountain, an old school friend of Megan's."

"I'm sure 'old' is the wrong word," Emlyn said, extending a hand.

The girl's hand fluttered out from the pocket of her anorak then bolted back to safety. Under the laced hood, her eyes looked shy.

Emlyn smiled. "Oh, congratulations on your new son, Tregelles, and your job, too."

Tregelles grunted, a mixture of embarrassment and modesty, then stared at the fire besoms stacked against the forestry perimeter.

"Tregelles has been enchanting me with names of conifers," Gweno-from-over-the-mountain said. Both men looked down at her in surprise. "At long last, I can tell a Sitka Spruce from a Japanese Larch!"

"David's Bones! I bet Emlyn Jenkins couldn't point you out a mountain ash!" Tregelles quipped. But Emlyn kept looking at the girl.

"Do you like trees?" he asked her.

"Well, yes. I think they're a neglected part of our heritage . . ."

"Gweno's a school teacher," Tregelles interrupted. "What she really means is that she's delighted to see real trees."

The girl caught his eye again briefly. Then she looked thoughtfully at her toecap, nudged some raindrops off a foxglove and continued:

"Yes, our education still tends to be rather secondhand, I'm afraid . . . nature pamphlets, text-book diagrams. Sometimes I think that education doesn't begin in earnest until we've left school."

"Perhaps we adults are just children gone astray," Emlyn said warmly, glad that Gweno hadn't allowed Tregelles to steamroller her.

124

"Do you visit this village much?" he asked, with a smile to encourage her.

"No. I'm staying with Tregelles and Megan until after the christening."

"There's a married couple driving down here tomorrow morning," Tregelles volunteered. "Godparents all the way from Bangor."

Gweno looked at Emlyn. "How about you? You've come even further. I don't suppose you'd have anything to come home for otherwise . . . Megan tells me you've been exiled in Durham."

Tregelles' eyebrows lifted sharply at the turn in conversation. He didn't give Emlyn a chance to reply.

"That's our Megan for you, she's started a fad now of keeping in touch with the outside world as she calls it." He tutted. "You'd think we were uncivilised here."

"Megan has a secret admiration for progressives," Gweno said sweetly. "She can see the advantages of the outside world."

Tregelles frowned, but took charge of the proceedings as usual. "Well, come on, Gweno, or our Megan will think we've lost our way. She's still old fashioned enough to worry and fret." He eyed Emlyn. "Perhaps you'd like to stop by for a cup of tea."

TREGELLES lived with his in-laws in a hydrangea-surrounded, granite house in Crimea Crescent. Emlyn remembered it well. He'd spent much of his boyhood and youth there, in one role or another.

"Come and see the baby first," Gweno suggested, and the three of them peered into the pram in the side porch. The baby was smiling in his sleep, one hand holding a fluffy lamb to his ear.

Emlyn reached in to stroke the baby's free hand but caught his cuff on a row of smirking ducks stretched across the pram hood. The toy ducks rattled hysterically.

"Shhhh!" Gweno said, face close to Emlyn's. "I rocked him for half an hour before he dropped off."

Emlyn grinned but thrust his hands apologetically into his pockets. "Think he favours anyone?" Tregelles asked him.

"He's going to be like his father, I think. He seems to have plenty of personality even in his sleep."

Tregelles grunted, but came close to smiling. "It's a wonder he gets any sleep at all with all the fuss indoors. You'd think we were going to have a coronation not a christening . . .!"

Emlyn saw what he meant as they entered the back door into the scullery. It was brimful of aunts and neighbours, all chattering discordantly and rattling teacups.

"Hello, stranger," Megan's mother hailed Emlyn across the room.

Gweno went off to find Megan. Tregelles took his coat and Emlyn was deserted amid the crowd of sceptical-looking women. There was nowhere for him to sit so he squatted down by the fire.

Megan's mother broke the sudden lull in conversation.

"Are they feeding you properly up in the North then?" she asked. She sounded civil but formal. "No, I suppose not, you've lost a lot of weight. Your aunt's not looking too strong just now, either . . ."

Emlyn found himself awkwardly parrying questions. It had once been expected that he himself would one day become a son-in-law in this house. Megan's mother had suffered quite a blow to her pride when Emlyn had evaded the inevitable. In this village, that rated almost as a sin, a chargeable offence. Now he felt appropriate uneasiness.

Gweno came back at last. "Megan's just coming."

Emlyn followed her gratefully into the hall.

Megan was coming downstairs with Tregelles. She stopped a few steps from the bottom to study him.

"Emlyn Jenkins, I'd never have believed it." She came down the last few stairs still shaking her head. "When you didn't come to our wedding we thought we'd never speak to you again — didn't we, Tregelles?"

Tregelles nodded, keeping close to her.

"There's no sense in you staying away for ever," she went on, "especially when you're looking so haggard!"

"Thanks," Emlyn said. "You look nice, too — as ever."

Megan smiled and Emlyn put his hand over his heart. "Are you giving me a royal pardon then, Megan?"

"Well." She stared dubiously at him. "A christening is supposed to be a time for new beginnings, isn't it?"

She ushered them into the parlour. "Here, let's us young ones have a secret cigarette." She winked. "Mam doesn't approve of me smoking. Tregelles, love, see if you can find that ashtray we locked up in our bedroom."

The parlour was cool — and cluttered. Carefully, Emlyn picked his way between piles of tissue paper, christening presents and pastry cartons as if he was crossing a minefield. He lowered himself into a chair and took a small package from his jacket.

"Oh, Megan, I thought silver would be appropriate . . ."

Megan tore off the wrapping paper, cooed over the christening gift and ran out to show it to the ladies next door. This gave Emlyn the chance to sit back and notice why Gweno looked so different.

She'd changed into a warm-coloured dress and was sitting elegantly opposite him now. In the forestry her anorak hood had concealed surprisingly thick hair, and the fledgling look had disappeared.

"You don't seem too comfortable on your home ground, Emlyn."

For a moment he was taken aback. Then he grinned wryly. "Well no, this is more like an away fixture for me . . . I've lost contact somewhere."

"Nothing in common?"

He shrugged. "Once I'd gone away, I had no particular wish to come back."

"Until now? Or is that just because of the christening?"

Emlyn thought for a minute. "I'm not sure," he said. "Perhaps I did want to see the place again."

Gweno blew a feather of cigarette smoke at the ceiling. "Sometimes I feel like breaking away myself, but . . . it takes courage. Megan's glad you came back."

"She's alone if she is." Emlyn grunted. "And I'm not too sure that she is . . ."

"That's unfair. People here may be suspicious, but it doesn't mean they're against you."

"Sorry, I was just feeling sorry for myself," Emlyn said.

126

She smiled. "Cheer up, you'll get a complex like that. Remember the old days. The holidays . . . the dances . . ."

Emlyn crossed his legs and fingered his chin thoughtfully. "Yes, those were good times all right . . . you're grinning . . . what's the matter?"

"Nothing I was merely admiring the dainty way that you drop ash everywhere."

Emlyn saw the funny side, too, furtively kneeling and brushing the cigarette ash from the immaculate carpet.

When Tregelles and Megan returned, respectively holding ashtray and tea-tray, they found Emlyn and Gweno both kneeling on the floor. Laughing they were.

WHAT OUR READERS SAID ON MEN . . .

I had missed the last bus and was walking home along an unlit road.

Suddenly I realised a man was following me. As I increased my pace he quickened his, and by the time I reached the main road I was running.

Feeling safe among other people, I waited for my pursuer to catch up, ready to give him a piece of my mind. To my astonishment, when he did appear he looked at me quite unabashed.

"I hope I didn't frighten you just now," he said. "But I just couldn't let you out of sight. I'm terrified of the dark."

At home my husband leaves his clothes all over the place for me to pick up. But if we go away from home and spend a few nights at a hotel (paying for the privilege) he picks everything up, folds his pyjamas and anything else that might be lying about.

His reason? "You can't expect maids to do that sort of thing. They have quite enough to do already!"

After a long argument with her husband, my cousin was adamant — their baby daughter was going to be called Louise.

Her husband didn't argue any more. Instead he hummed the song "Louise" all evening, every now and then giving a deep, mysterious sigh.

At last my cousin grew curious and asked him what it was all about.

After a lot of wheedling he "admitted" that Louise was the name of an ex-girlfriend.

The baby was christened Helen.

Every night before he goes to bed, my husband sets three alarm clocks to go off at 10-minute intervals. This is in case he doesn't hear the first ring, so there are still two others to waken him (he hopes).

He is also a great believer in auto-suggestion. After the clock auto-suggestion. After the clock episode, he "writes" the desired time on his forehead with his finger and repeats the "writing" with his big toe on the sheets at the foot of the bed!

127

THE Sunday of the christening was sunny. The chapel bell woke Emlyn. Glad to be rid of the grey clouds and dirty drizzle, he got up early and took his time in the bathroom, whistling as he shaved.

He came down to breakfast in a dressing-gown and found Aunt Anna hanging his new suit and white shirt before the fire.

"I pressed your suit, Emlyn, you'd packed it awkward. There's sensible material, too." Nervously she ran a finger along his suit lapel. "You bought this suit for the christening, didn't you?"

"That's right. I was lucky to get one to fit at such short notice . . ."

"It must have used up a lot of your college grant, Emlyn." She paused to gather courage. "Your uncle left me comfortable enough, you know . . . I could always help out a bit. I know you always tried to stand on your own feet, especially after your mam and dad . . ."

"Don't worry, love. I worked last vacation, saved some pocket money. There are mines in the North, too."

"You worked with coal — up there?"

"In a mining village just like this one. I've even got friends there!" On impulse he stooped and kissed his aunt on the forehead.

"Well I'm blessed!" she said breathlessly and went into the scullery to finish preparing breakfast.

They had brown boiled eggs in the egg-cups with knitted covers. The home-baked bread was like snow, the farm butter crinkly yellow. All the cups and plates were family heirlooms preserved for special occasions.

The sudden, urgent rapping of the brass doorknocker stopped his meandering. He rose from the table, but his aunt was already showing Tregelles through the hall. Tregelles looked grave, stopped muttering in Welsh and stood with his back to the fire.

"Tregelles just had some bad news, Emlyn," Aunt Anna said. "Another telegram."

Tregelles frowned, like the Black Mountain during a storm. "Our Megan should have had more sense than to ask a couple from Bangor to be godparents. People get so undependable when they move away!"

"It's flu they've got then?" Aunt Anna asked.

"Yes, both sick and can't travel." Tregelles looked up at Emlyn. "Ay, we've been let down badly. Emlyn Jenkins . . . I'm here to ask you a favour."

He hesitated, shifted his feet and rolled up his cap. "I was wondering — we were wondering — if you could see your way clear to — to helping our baby like. We've already got a godmother, of course, Gweno. It's not usual to have a single girl or a bachelor either, but in the circumstances — could you stand for us? Be godfather?"

Emlyn stared at them both. "But the christening, it's this afternoon — I mean . . ." He looked down at his slippers.

"Yes, Tregelles," he said quietly and looked up. "I'd be proud to."

EMLYN came out of the chapel after the christening and blinked in the bright sunlight.

The chapel had been packed and the roof had seemed ready to come off with the fervent singing and the minister's fiery Welsh address.

It had overwhelmed Emlyn. He'd stood among his own kind, singing half-remembered hymns until he had felt goose-pimples of emotion.

Something Megan had said the previous day had come back again and again to him: *Christenings are a time for new beginnings.* A time, too, for re-birth of friendships, death of old prejudices.

Gweno had been standing close to him during the ceremony carefully holding the baby. When the minister had wetted the baby's head a solitary cry of protest had rung through the chapel.

Gweno, over-anxious, had got into difficulty with the baby's christening robe. As it had threatened to unwind, she'd turned to Emlyn for assistance. He'd reached over and tucked in the loose folds.

He'd felt clumsy though everyone had eyes only for the infant — except Gweno perhaps. He'd noticed how fresh she'd looked among the ranks of camphored costumes, severe suits, revered hymn books . . .

"It wasn't too painful, was it, Emlyn?" Gweno's voice came to him as he stood blinking in the sunlight.

He turned. "I was just thinking about you."

"That's nice."

"Very."

Tregelles and Megan had been posing outside the chapel for photographs with the baby. Now they called through the crowd.

"Hey, godparents, your turn. Come and have your picture taken before we go back for tea. Your Aunt Anna, too, Emlyn."

Emlyn insisted on standing between Gweno and his aunt.

"Put your arm round them both!" Tregelles bawled good-humouredly from the back.

"Hush, you'll frighten the baby!" Emlyn said but took Tregelles' advice anyway. The photographer was fiddling with his tripod and keeping the spectators at bay.

"You look a real gentleman, Emlyn," his aunt said. "Don't you think so, Gweno?"

"He would do if he stopped long enough in one place for us to see him," she replied, flicking an imaginary speck from his lapel.

"Stand still, please," the photographer pleaded.

"They certainly look nice together," Megan called out from somewhere in the crowd.

Aunt Anna smiled past the camera and away over the years.

"Wouldn't it be nice now . . . ?" she started saying as the photographer disappeared beneath his old-fashioned black hood.

"Wouldn't what be nice, love?" Emlyn prompted.

"Well, if Gweno could call and see us next time . . . when you come home again."

Emlyn concentrated on the concertina camera. "I was thinking actually about this evening. The Pressdees will be crowded out with all the christening guests. Could Gweno come to supper with us in Sebastapol Street?"

Emlyn's aunt was frozen in pose, but she managed a quick snort. "Well ask the girl — or you'll never know."

Emlyn turned his head sharply and asked Gweno's profile. "Well, how about it, Gweno? Tonight?"

"Smile, please!" the photographer coaxed.

But Gweno's smile needed no bidding.

The End.

I

**That's all he ever was —
"somebody else's brat" to the folk he had
to live with. And so Joey prayed for
a miracle . . .**

TO Joey, South Africa was the Diggings, and the Diggings was the world. Everyone he had ever known in his seven years of life had worked a claim at the Diggings.

They lived in the mud and corrugated-iron houses which blemished the landscape like pimples on an unlovely face. At night the men came home and got drunk and fought with their wives, and the women didn't mind for they knew that things had gone badly for their men again that day.

Things usually went badly at the Diggings, especially for Joey. That was life, and he knew life to be savage and comfortless and ugly. Life meant being cold in the winter; it meant thorns in the soles of your bare feet and never quite enough food. It meant living with *Them*.

They weren't his parents. His mother had died when he was born, and his father had been killed in a road accident three years ago, and so Joey had been sent to live with *Them*.

She was his mother's sister, and her name was Dora. She wouldn't let Joey call her auntie because she said it made her feel old and blowzy. So he called her just Dora when he spoke to her, but in his mind he mostly called her "she."

She was different from the othe women at the Diggings. She dye her hair yellow and painted her mout a deep red colour and wore brigh dresses with beads sewn over th front.

She hadn't any children of her ow — didn't want any, thank you very much, she said. Just look how you figure went to pot after only one baby.

He was called Abel, and he didn' want children, either. He had enough on his plate, by God, providing fo someone else's brat. That was how Abel talked — in a loud voice with lot of swear words.

He was big and strong, the strong est man at the Diggings, and very proud of his body. He walked aroun in his vest a lot so that people could see his muscles.

Joey thought about *Them* as he walked home from school. *She* wasn' too bad, for as long as he didn't make a noise or bother her, she didn't take too much notice of him.

But *He* was different. He didn't like kids, and if he was in one of his moods he picked on Joey. Joey wished with all his might that Abel wouldn't be home this afternoon.

He walked slowly, ploughing up the loose sand with his bare toes, keeping his shoulders hunched and

JUST JOEY

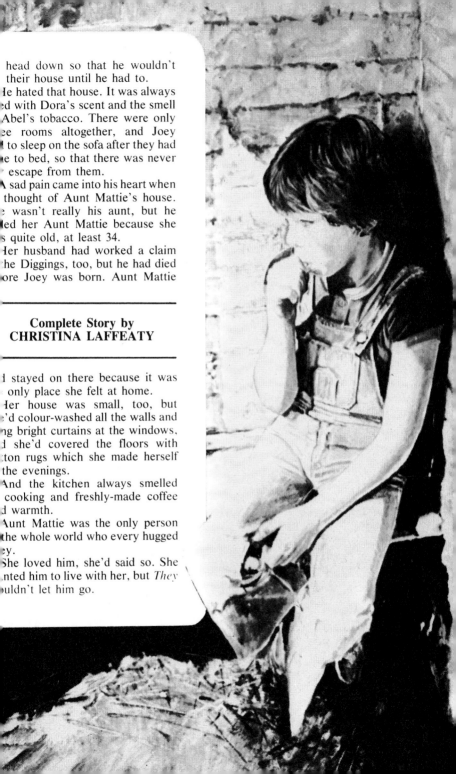

head down so that he wouldn't
their house until he had to.

He hated that house. It was always
ed with Dora's scent and the smell
Abel's tobacco. There were only
ee rooms altogether, and Joey
to sleep on the sofa after they had
e to bed, so that there was never
escape from them.

A sad pain came into his heart when
thought of Aunt Mattie's house.
e wasn't really his aunt, but he
led her Aunt Mattie because she
s quite old, at least 34.

Her husband had worked a claim
he Diggings, too, but he had died
ore Joey was born. Aunt Mattie

**Complete Story by
CHRISTINA LAFFEATY**

---

stayed on there because it was
only place she felt at home.

Her house was small, too, but
'd colour-washed all the walls and
ng bright curtains at the windows,
she'd covered the floors with
ton rugs which she made herself
the evenings.

And the kitchen always smelled
cooking and freshly-made coffee
warmth.

Aunt Mattie was the only person
the whole world who every hugged
y.

She loved him, she'd said so. She
nted him to live with her, but *They*
uldn't let him go.

"It's the money, of course," Aunt Mattie had muttered once.

When she saw Joey looking at her she'd smiled and said, "The man who ran your pa down had to pay compensation, and they get money every week while you're staying with them. They must find it a big help, with Abel not doing so well out of his claim."

Although Joey was sad at the thought that he could never live with Aunt Mattie, it had given him a lovely feeling of importance to know about the money.

He had mentioned the money once. Abel was going on and on about Joey scuffing the toes of his Sunday shoes, saying that shoes didn't grow on trees and that he was spending enough money on Joey as it was.

When Joey muttered something about the money, and Abel had said to Dora, "One of these days I'll knock this cheeky brat right into he middle of next week." So Joey had never mentioned it again, but he'd thought about it a lot.

THE afternoon was hot and the sand scorched the soles of his feet, so he stopped to wade through the stream. He could see his reflection, drunken and distorted, in the moving water, his thin legs like two bent sticks shivering in the stream.

Only a little way now, he thought reluctantly, and then he'd be home.

But first he had to look for a wishing stone.

He couldn't remember if someone had told him about wishing stones or if it was just something he had known about all his life, but each afternoon, for as long as he could remember, he'd searched through the pebbles in the stream for a wishing stone.

There was no particular shape or colour to a wishing stone — it was just different. Few people ever found one. Joey had never known anyone who had. A wishing stone was magic, like God. It made everything possible for the person who possessed it.

Just old brown pebbles again, he thought, with the familiar dull disappointment. Just ordinary, old, brown pebbles.

Then he saw it, and his hands darted eagerly into the water, thrusting the brown pebbles out of his way.

It wasn't very large, and it had no particular shape or colour, but it was different all right. It might be a wishing stone.

He clutched it tightly in his fist and ran the rest of the way home. He had to test it the first chance he got, to see if it was a real wishing stone.

Abel was there when Joey got to the house.

"You're home, are you?" he said. "About time, too. Where've you been loafing all afternoon?"

I wish, Joey said silently to the wishing stone, I wish Abel would go away.

"I'd give you what-for," Abel said in his loud voice, "if I didn't have to go out. Another time you won't get away with it, hear me?" And he slammed the door.

It worked, Joey thought dizzily. It really worked!

She was lying on the sofa painting her nails to match her lips.

"You ask for trouble, don't you?" she said without looking up. "Your food's in the oven, and count yourself lucky that I bothered to save it for you."

132

I wish, Joey whispered to the wishing stone, searching for the most wildly unlikely thing he could think of, I wish it could be meat-balls.

And it was!

Joey ate the food without tasting it, his left hand fondling the wishing stone in his pocket. I could do anything, he thought exultantly. I could have a bomb drop on both of them — or I could make Dora's figure go to pot by letting her have a baby — or — or I could have someone give Abel a black eye — no, two black eyes. I could do anything!

"I want you to go to the store," Dora said. "Get bread and lard, and ask if that hair-stuff of mine has come in yet. The money's on the dresser."

He took the money and went outside. The world was no longer a huddle of ugly shacks in a setting of red dust — it was beautiful, beautiful. He would never be afraid again, never be alone again, never be hungry again. He had a wishing stone.

He bought the bread and the lard and the shopwoman said yes, Dora's hair-stuff had come in and it would be half a crown.

Joey thought, all at once, that here was one small revenge he could have right now, just for a start.

"I'll leave the hair-stuff," he told the shopwoman. "She said just to ask. I want sweets, please, for half a crown."

The shopwoman wouldn't sell him any sweets at first, but he said it was his birthday and they'd given him the money to spend as he liked.

HE took the bread and the lard and a great paper bag of sweets to the stream, and he stayed there until it grew dark, eating his sweets and thinking of the many things he meant to wish for with his wishing stone.

He wasn't afraid at all when he went home, even though Abel was there and in one of his bad moods.

"Where the devil have you been all this time?" he shouted as soon as Joey came into the kitchen.

"And where's my hair-stuff?" Dora wanted to know, grabbing the parcel of bread and lard from him.

Joey stood with his back against the wall. "I didn't get the hair-stuff. I bought sweets with the money."

"Sweets!" Abel shouted, his face growing red and swollen and terrible. "You rotten little thief, I'll —"

"I'm not a thief!" Joey cried shrilly. "I'm not! It was my half-crown by rights, out of my money!"

"This time," Abel yelled to Dora, "this time the cheeky brat has got to be taught a lesson."

He made a lunge at Joey, grabbing him by the shoulders. Joey's hand delved into his pocket for the wishing stone.

"I hate you!" he shouted. "And I wish I could live with Aunt Mattie instead of here. I wish — "

Abel spun Joey around with one hand while the other fumbled with his belt. Joey dropped the wishing stone. It rolled across the floor and underneath the sofa, and Joey scrambled free and went to find it.

Abel lunged forward to catch hold of Joey again, and then he saw the wishing stone.

"Where did you get that?" he asked slowly.

"It's mine," Joey muttered, his fingers closing over the wishing stone. "I found it."

"Give it to me." Abel bent Joey's fingers back, took the wishing stone, and carried it over to the lamp.

"My God," he said softly. "My God!"

Joey began to cry. "Give me back my wishing stone!"

"Shut your trap," Abel said, but he wasn't really paying attention to Joey. "Come and look at this," he called to Dora.

Together they stared at the wishing stone while Joey stood in the corner crying.

"My God," Abel said again in a funny voice. "All these years I've been sweating blood; all these years I've been grubbing in the mud, praying for one even half the size of his, and the brat walks about with one in his pocket! Look at it, will you! It's worth — oh, thousands!"

"We'll have a house in Jo'burg," Dora said, her eyes shining. "No, a flat — with a cocktail cabinet — and we'll throw parties — "

Abel grabbed her by the waist and spun her around.

"And I'll have the biggest damn car you've ever seen."

"I'll have a fur coat," Dora cried breathlessly. "And one of those diamond cocktail watches — and a white poodle."

"It's *my* wishing stone," Joey shouted. "I found it!" He flung himself at them, beating at them with his fists.

Abel pushed him away impatiently, but Dora said slowly, "The kid — we forgot about the kid. What will we do with him?"

Abel looked at Joey. "Blast, yes, we don't want the brat under our feet now. "Tell you what, we'll let Mattie have him. That's it, he can go and live with Mattie."

A ND so Joey's wish, the last one he had ever made on the wishing stone, came true. He was thinking about this as Aunt Mattie tucked him into bed in the first bedroom he had ever had for his very own.

"Sleep well," she said, looking down at him with shining eyes. "Oh, we'll have such good times together, Joey! I'm so thankful your uncle found that diamond on his claim."

"It wasn't an old diamond," Joey said. "It was my wishing stone, and he stole it."

His eyes filled with tears. "Abel took it away with him, and it was mine."

Aunt Mattie shook her head, and then she gave that little smile which grown-ups give when they don't believe a word you've said.

"Never mind, Joey. I have a box somewhere, with pebbles I found at the seaside when I was a girl. We'll look for it tomorrow, and maybe you'll find another wishing stone among them."

Joey gazed at her sadly. He loved Aunt Mattie and he was very glad he could live with her from now on, but she didn't understand.

It was one of the things about wishing stones that no-one got a second chance. If he searched until he was a hundred he would never find one again.

The End.

Complete story by ELSIE ALEXANDER

Postman's Knock

When neighbours
fall out it's as well
to have all the
evidence down in
black and white!

Flat Three

Dear Sir,
   Since you took over the flat above me, exactly five days ago,
I have to report the following:
   (A) My clock has stopped.
   (B) I have had continual ear-ache.
   (C) I have fallen three times over a laundry bag left on the
       stairs. Repeat — LEFT THREE TIMES ON THE STAIRS.
   (D) Four pieces of plaster (large) have fallen on my head.
   (E) "Oklahoma," which formerly I loved, I now detest.
   (F) Constant bellowing (yours, I presume) to Clara has torn
       my nerves to shreds. If your wife is so deaf, may I
       suggest a hearing-aid?
Kindly look into these matters at your earliest convenience
and oblige.
                                    Your neighbour,
                                    Jennifer E. Jones.

P.S. Very efficient hearing-aids can be obtained from
     Brown's in Park Road.

Dear Madam,

Your letter of the 18th. inst. to hand this morning, and I am happy to reply as follows:

(A) Since I have never so much as looked at your clock, I cannot be held responsible for its decease.

(B) I understand that wax frequently accumulates in the ear. Daily washing is recommended.

(C) As the laundry-bag, (victim, I suspect, of a passing stilletto heel) has now been efficiently repaired, I have decided not to carry the matter of damages any further.

(D) Loose plaster would indicate, to the intelligent, a need for re-plastering.

(E) Rogers and Hammerstein, creators of this wonderful work, would, no doubt, be most upset but, of course, being men, would realise that women are notoriously fickle.

(F) You will be relieved to know that Clara is not deaf— on the contrary, her hearing is very acute. And, I might add, with all modesty, that my voice is sweet music in her ears.

Trusting that I have been of some assistance to you and assuring you of my best attention at all times.

Yours faithfully
John J. Smith

P.S. I am glad you find your hearing-aid efficient.

Dear Sir,   Flat Three

Although not, by any means, lacking in a sense of humour, I find your facetiousness quite out of place. May I reply very briefly and to the point?

I am NOT dirty. I am NOT un-intelligent. I am NOT fickle. And I do NOT use a hearing-aid (though there have been times during the last few days when ear PLUGS would have been helpful)!

My clock is again going nicely. Kindly see that it continues to do so.

If you leave your laundry IN THE LOWER HALL, it will be collected.

Thanking you for your attention.

Yours faithfully,
Jennifer E. Jones.

P.S. Your wife's taste in music though incredible, does not concern me.

FLAT FOUR

Dear Madam,
Your further letter to hand. I shall be most happy to see your clock — when do you wish me to call?
Yours faithfully,
John J. Smith

P.S. In the two years since Clara became mine, she has responded well to my training.

Dear Sir, Flat Three
I not NOT wish you to call upon me. Personally I think you are insufferable.
Yours faithfully,
Jennifer E. Jones
May
P.S. My I offer my sympathy to your wife in her GREAT AFFLICATION? And my clock has stopped again!

Dear Madam,
I shall call upon you today at 6 p.m. complete with tools etc.
If however, this is inconvenient to you, kindly put the offending clock on the stairs.
Since MY eyesight is particularly good, I shall not fall over it.
Yours faithfully
John J. Smith

P.S. Clara wishes to accompany me — do you mind?

My dear Mr. Smith, Flat Three
May I thank you for repairing my clock so efficiently? Also for your very kind offer to repair my ceiling.
Would Saturday suit you as I am at home all day then? I would be delighted if you would share lunch with me too.
Yours sincerely
Jennifer E. Jones
P.S. I CAN cook, even if I AM un-intelligent etc. etc.
P.P.S. Isn't Clara sweet?

My dear Miss Jones,
      Thank you. I shall be delighted.
                       Yours very sincerely
                          John J. Smith

    P.S. I hope so.
    P.P.S. Yes, isn't she?

Flat Three

Dear John,
      My ceiling looks beautiful. My clock is going again.
By the way, that window cord has been broken ever since
I came here. It is lovely to have it repaired at last.
      You have been most kind and I do appreciate it.
                      Yours gratefully
                      Jennifer
P.S. Has "Oklahoma" met its end? I do miss it so.

My dear Jennifer,
      I am sorry to say that "Oklahoma" developed a certain
flatness about two weeks ago and can only regain its former
tunefulness if you come up and listen.
      Will you lunch here on Sunday, please? (Clara thinks
I am a fabulous cook.)
      Perhaps we could have a run in the car after lunch?
Clara dislikes motoring and much prefers a chair by the fire.
                    Till Sunday, I am
                    Yours,
                    John.

Flat Three

John dear,
      Wasn't Sunday lovely? The girls in the office said it
rained all day — I didn't see any, did you?
      I'll tell you a secret. I've always dreamed of someone
tall and dark and handsome — like you John! Funny
isn't it?

      I do hope you don't prefer blondes, John dear!
You don't, do you? I always been red — but, thank
goodness, I've no freckles now.

      Give Clara my love. Do you know, I've always
wanted a Siamese cat — isn't that queer? Do you think
she really likes me, John?

                    Yours
                    Jennifer

P.S. I love you, dear.

FLAT FOUR

Darling Jennifer,
    I'm answering your sweet letter straight away:
(1) Yes. (2) No. (3) Yes. (4) No (5) Not at all. (6) Sure.
                                    Your Own,
                                    John

P.S. You've got FIVE dear little freckles on your dear little nose!

John Darling,   Flat Three
    You wretch! Call THAT a love letter! It's evident
you believe in actions! Who nibbled my ear last night?
Not Clara, I know. The sweet!
    My ring is gorgeous. I lay awake all last night
- or nearly all - just touching it, while you snored
upstairs. Do you snore, darling?
    A teeny-weeny piece of ceiling came down last
night - could you come soon, please?
                                    All my love
                                    Gennifer

P.S. I have not!

FLAT FOUR

Darling,
    Honestly, Jennifer! Do you take a hammer to that ceiling?
                                    Yours
                                    John

Darling John,   Flat Three
            Yes.
        All my love
        Gennifer

The End

The Eccentric Mr B.

You couldn't have a world of just Mr B's. But you wouldn't have much of a world without a few of his kind.

I ENTERED the office of Mr Blundell, exporter.

"Oh, Carol —" Mr B. said.

"Ah," I said, "so it's a favour. Not Miss Newton — but Carol!"

"Well, ye-es, it *is* a favour, as a matter of fact."

"You want me to work during lunch!"

"Time and a half," Mr Blundell said quickly. "Look, I got this young fellow coming to see me, has his own little business, already. I want he contract to us the sole exporting rights."

Mr B.'s English, like himself, has a Continental flavour.

"So . . . I'm taking him to lunch, just as soon as he gets here, and I want you should go along with us. A lovely lady secretary don't hurt business."

He gave me his best persuasive leer.

I didn't mind, because he only leers at friends. And besides, he's the fatherly type.

"I like you, too," I told him. "So I'll do it. And talking of business —"

"If I get the contract, you won't lose," he assured me.

Mr B. is shrewd, but he's scrupulously fair; which is more than can be said for some of his competitors.

Anyway, I reckoned I'd be doing this "young fellow" a favour by helping him make up his mind to contract with us.

And that's how I met Ralph.

HE was nice, and we got the contract. And the next time he had an appointment with us, Mr Blundell had an urgent matter to attend to on the other side of the city.

"Why don't you take Mr Dalton to lunch for me," Mr Blundell said slyly. "So beautiful! Why you're not married yet is beyond me."

"Because I haven't met the man I'd fancy having breakfast with for the rest of my life," I told him.

"You know something, it's the truth!" he exclaimed, spreading his arms wide to embrace it. "It's the very truth! Out of the mouths of babes, the very acid test."

"Oh, come now. I'm twenty-seven."

"Ah!" he exclaimed, knocking his head with the palm of his hand. "The pity of it!"

Complete Story by ANNE CARR

A suspicion suddenly rose inside me. I looked at him more closely.

"You're not trying your hand at match-making, are you by any chance?"

"Now why should I do such a thing as that, please tell me?"

"All right, I will. Because you think it would be lovely to have a nice new secretary — one who didn't know all your funny stories."

"Such a thing! Entertain the gentleman, and charge it, and tell him I'll be back directly after lunch. Walk him in the park — anything — only keep him —"

The rest of it got lost in the revolving door as he hurried out.

AFTER lunch we walked in the park, and Ralph told me he was a widower, and had a daughter aged nine.

Let that teach you to beware of labels, I told myself sternly. Because, until then, the word "widower" had always conjured up for me a picture of a drab, colourless, empty man.

Ralph was not like that at all. He was warm flesh and blood, and tall, with kind eyes, and nice teeth, and a pleasant voice.

In fact, being with Ralph was being home, and home's a pretty good place to be.

But . . . a nine-year-old daughter!

After a few more meetings, I said to myself —

"Well — so what?"

And still later —

"I wouldn't care if he had six children, all juvenile delinquents . . ."

So when he asked me to marry him, I didn't hesitate a second.

"Oh, yes — yes, darling," I said.

I learned that Ralph and his daughter lived in a service flat, in the care of a motherly widow who had answered Ralph's ad. for a housekeeper.

"Both my wife's parents and my own live up north," he explained. "My business is here, and I wanted Vivien to have a real home, with me."

I admired the way he had coped with his problems, and resolved to make up for everything, as far as I could, to both of them.

But it didn't work out. The child didn't take to me at all.

She didn't want any part of this strange woman who was to usurp her mother's place.

I suppose the housekeeper was different as she was so much older. And I could see Vivien's point of view. If my mother had died when I was Vivien's age, I wouldn't have taken kindly to some other person coming into my home as my father's wife.

But how to get through to her?

Ralph and I both tried very hard. We took her to theatre and seaside, funfair and secluded lake. She was always meticulously polite to me, but never unfroze.

I thought about it. You have a problem. You can't solve it. So what do you do?

You ask for help. Where?

I WENT to Mr Blundell.

"Here's your coffee," I said. "And I sent out for some of your favourite mocha cakes."

He laid down his pen. "Aha!" he said. "It's yet only half past ten! So it's a favour you want."

"You have a suspicious mind!"

"So?"

"As a matter of fact, it is a favour. I have a problem."

"I knew that, too. You've been looking porous."

That knocked me off balance.

"Porous?" I said.

"Yes. You know — poring over something or other."

I smiled.

"Not laughing," Mr B. said. "So it's serious."

"Well, it is to me," I admitted. "When I started working for you, you told me that if ever I had a problem of any kind, I could bring it to you. Did you really mean that, or is it merely something you say to all the girls?"

"I say it to all the girls." Mr B. nodded. "And I mean it. Stop running around the bush, and tell me."

He heard me right through without interrupting once, which surprised me. When I'd finished he leaned back in his chair.

"So. You go right back to work, and I'll think about it."

I felt as if a load had been lifted off my mind, and sat down to drink my coffee.

Presently he buzzed me.

"I'd like to meet this Vivien," he told me, "and then I'll know better what to do."

It sounded reasonable.

"So we'll have a picnic," he went on. "Tell her your boss is giving a

picnic, and she's especially invited. Do you think she'll come with you, without her father?"

"She will if Ralph tells her to —"

ON Saturday afternoon Ralph lent me his car, and I drove Vivien to the spot where we were to meet Mr Blundell.

Ralph had been a bit doubtful about letting us go off on our own, but he liked my boss. Mr Blundell was one of those who got away from Nazi Germany before the war. He never talked about it, but I guessed he had faced problems beside which mine would seem petty.

I think some of my faith in him had rubbed off on Ralph. Besides, we were both ready to try almost anything.

The day was fine, the spot delightful: a flat, soft-grassed riverbank, secluded by tall hedges, with pleasant woods upriver on both sides.

Mr B. had not arrived, and Vivien and I started to lay out the cloth and things in readiness.

She was gravely polite, as always, but there wasn't any real warmth between us. She was merely putting up with me.

However, we both became absorbed in our task; until suddenly, as I knelt by the basket, I became aware that we were no longer alone.

I glanced up, expecting to see Mr Blundell, and found myself gazing at two tough-looking boys in leather jackets.

One of them broke the ominous silence. In a derisive voice he said, "Oh, look! It's a pic-nic!"

"A girlie pic-nic," the other added.

Number One was eyeing the three sets of dishes.

"Expecting someone, then?"

"I'm expecting —" I glanced at Vivien. "My husband."

"Doesn't look as though he's coming, like."

"He *is* coming," Vivien said stoutly. She drew closer to me as I stood up.

"Shall we join 'em?" Number One asked.

"Nah — take too long. Somebody might turn up. Let's just chuck their stuff in the river."

Number Two said this quite casually.

"I got a better idea. Let's have a bit of fun with the pretty girl."

The first one had been edging closer, and suddenly made a snatch at Vivien's scarf. I guessed that this was just a gambit. He knew that if he touched her, I'd try to intervene; and it was me he wanted to tangle with.

Vivien was scared half to death.

She screamed and dodged, and in that instant I snatched up the carving knife from the picnic cloth and sprang to her side.

"You so much as lay a finger on her," I said between my teeth, "and so help me, I'll use this!"

The knife was long, pointed and sharp, and he looked a little uneasy.

"She your kid sister, then?"

"No, she's not!" I exploded. "*She's my daughter!*"

"What's going on, there?"

The shout came from the direction of the road, and with the greatest relief I've ever felt in my life, I saw Mr Blundell positively galloping down upon us, brandishing a heavy walking stick over his head.

It seemed that the combination of Mr Blundell's stick and my knife were too much for the two young thugs to take. They hared off.

Mr B. charged after them.

"Louterers!" he yelled, his English flying all to pieces. "Loafs! Cowards!" He made pounding motions with his stick. "I'll chastise you within an inch of —"

As he vanished around a turn of the path in the woods, my knees suddenly turned to water, and I sank down on to the soft grass, pulling Vivien across my lap.

PRESENTLY she pulled away and looked at me tearfully. "Carol, would you really have hurt that man if he'd touched me?"

"Well," I admitted, "I'd certainly have stabbed him a few times!"

We laughed together.

"Stay here," I said, getting up. "I must go and see if Mr Blundell is all right."

"Don't leave me!" Vivien begged.

Sweet, sweet music!

"Don't worry, poppet," I told her, kissing the top of her head. "I won't be a minute, and then I'll be around for ever more."

Worriedly I hurried across the grass and into the wood. Suddenly, from behind a clump of bushes I heard Mr Blundell's voice.

"There you are, boys. Five pounds each, and the best money you'll ever earn in your lives!"

I stealthily parted some leaves and saw him handing over money to the two louts.

"I don't feel so good about this, Mr Blundell," Number One said. "If I didn't know you so well —"

"They seemed like real nice people," Number Two chipped in.

"People, shmeeple!" Mr B. said. "I tell you, not to worry! I told you the story, and I told you what to do. And like a charm it worked.

"When I looked through the bushes, yet, they were cuddling each other like crazy! If you don't believe, only come and look —"

They found themselves staring into my grim face.

"*So?*" I said in dark accusation.

But after the first moment of dismay, Mr B. was unabashed.

"Who is eating *you* all up, young lady? Did you ever have it so better?

"Didn't I say I would make it all right? And haven't I? And if not, kindly tell me who was kissing who a few moments ago, please, I'd like to know?"

"You engineered this whole affair," I said, breathing hard.

He held up a placating hand.

"Please. Please. A long time ago I learned it — there's nothing like a common danger for uniting families —"

"Carol —" Vivien called from somewhere behind me.

"You'd better go," Mr Blundell said grandly. "Your family's shouting you already."

"Coming, darling," I called in reply.

But I kissed Mr Blundell before I ran back to her.

The End.

K

A Touch Of Understanding

It had happened to her once before. Only this time the ending would be different.

JUST look at it — isn't it awful?'' Barry groaned, gazing at the cottage in deep dismay. "Mother, I can't let Rita come here!"

Mary Fenton had to agree. Even in the mellow autumn sunlight the little house, with its bird's nest thatch, sunken door, and windows like blind eyes, did not seem the right setting for a modern young married couple like Rita and Barry.

"It may not be so bad inside," she said hopefully, and glanced at his frowning face.

How like his father he was, with those deep blue eyes, the firm, thrusting chin, the rugged good looks. Her heart had been singing, "Barry's home — Barry's home — for good!"

" 'Accommodation provided' — that's what Mr Mason said," Barry grumbled. "He calls this accommodation! I've a good mind to tell him he can keep his job!"

Mary put a restraining hand on his arm.

"Let's go in," she said hastily, tucking a tendril of hair under the brim of her coral hat. With his quick temper, he might resign from his new job as head forester, then she'd lose him again. And she couldn't bear that. She just couldn't!

Barry thrust the huge key into the keyhole and the door creaked open. A damp smell came to meet them, and Mary sank her chin deeper into her fur collar against the chill. Her slate-blue eyes studied the long room with its brooding wallpaper, sad paint, and low ceiling.

"Thank heaven Rita and Nigel are flying over later," Barry said, stalking into another bleak room. "If Nigel hadn't caught measles they'd be here now, seeing it like this. But perhaps —'' He paused thoughtfully.

With a sense of guilt Mary remembered how glad she had been when Barry bounced through the Customs alone. Oh, yes, she had gone with Hugh to the airport in a welter of apprehension, joy, and hunger. Apprehension at meeting the stranger who had won Barry's heart, joy at having Barry home, hunger for a glimpse of her two-year-old grandson. Yet determined to greet Rita with warmth and love.

The girl's absence had been like a reprieve. For a few days at least she could listen to Barry's deep voice, free from the nagging fear that she was taking up too much of his time.

"You can do it, can't you, Mother?"

Barry's question snapped her thoughts back. Puzzled, she glanced into his worried face.

**Complete
Story by
FLORENCE
LEDGER**

"Do what?" she asked.

His sweeping gesture included the entire cottage. "Make this place fit to live in. You know — paint, paper, furniture. We had a furnished house in Sierra Leone, and I've shipped only personal stuff — wedding gifts, and that sort of thing. You would have to start from scratch."

Mary felt the colour surge into her cheeks. Staring at his now pleading face, she said helplessly, "But I don't know what Rita likes. I'm sure she'd rather choose everything herself."

"That would take months!" he burst out. "And with the new baby due in December, Rita just couldn't cope."

He gave Mary his most winning smile, put an arm round her shoulder.

"You've such good taste," he coaxed. "Anything you did would please Rita. I'm sure of it. She wouldn't take offence. She never does."

CAREFULLY Mary studied the room. What would she do if the cottage were hers? Scrape the painted beams and polish them to their original gloss; choose striped paper to give the room height, pastels to defeat the gloom and gleaming copper to bring warmth to the dull stone fireplace.

Even as she considered the possibilites, her thoughts slipped back through the years to the day she herself had landed in England piloting three small sons.

She had left the small Canadian town regretfully, but without tears, for she was going to Hugh, to the "old country" he had talked about so often during their first years of marriage. Full of shining hopes she had looked upon it as a Great Adventure, discovering England with Hugh, making new friends.

Hugh had flown over to settle his father's estate, been offered a good position and accepted without consulting her. He had great faith in himself and faith in her love.

When the ship docked at Liverpool, Hugh had rushed on board, swooped her into his arms, and kissed her joyfully. The boys tugged his jacket, clamouring for attention, and he had released her and listened to their chatter.

All eagerness, she raised her voice above theirs. "You've found good lodgings for us?"

"Better than that!" He chuckled. "A house, all furnished!"

"Oh, lovely! Better for the children. Will you be able to get time off later for house hunting?"

"We won't have to house hunt, darling. This house belongs to us!"

Stunned, she'd stared at him. "You mean you've bought one without waiting to see if I'd like it?"

"You'll love it!" he enthused. "It's my old home, darling. You won't have to do a thing but get settled in."

"But, Hugh —" she began to protest then caught the anguished looks on the boys' faces and stifled angry words.

All the way to the bustling Midlands town a dark flame of resentment burned in her brain. She had tried desperately to fight against it. Oh, God, she prayed, let me like the house! Let us all be happy in it. That's all that matters, really.

But the gaunt semi-detached house at the end of a row of exactly similar houses brought tears to her eyes. She'd been so happy, now everything was spoiled. How could she live in a house with a tiny, fenced-in front garden? How could the children stand it after being accustomed to the wide open spaces at home in Canada?

His arm around her waist, Hugh had guided her up the narrow garden path.

"This is our new home, darling. And here's Mother waiting —"

Mary found herself looking at a thin-faced woman with tight lips, a sharp chin, and faded blue eyes. A cool voice said, "Tea's ready!" and Mrs Fenton, after a brief glance at the boys, had turned back into the house.

Slowly Mary followed her. She had meant to kiss her mother-in-law and say how happy she was to meet her. But the forbidding expression in Mrs Fenton's eyes, the abruptness of her welcome, had cast a chill over her heart.

INSIDE, the place appalled her. The furniture was hideously old fashioned, the wallpaper gloomy, the curtains brown chenille, the carpet garishly floral. Mrs Fenton took her place at the head of the Victorian table and began to pour from a silver teapot.

Simmering inside, Mary waited until old Mrs Fenton left, and the children were in bed. Then a torrent of words poured from her.

"I can't live with this!" she stormed. "It's awful! Imagine — horsehair — in this day and age! I won't have it! If we're going to stay in this ghastly house we'll have to make it more modern!"

"But, darling, what would Mother think? She'd be terribly upset. After all, she's been kind enough to give us her home. She didn't have to, but Elsie and Roger asked her to live with them across town."

"Well, Elsie or anyone else can have it — woodworm and all!"

"What does the furniture matter?" Hugh demanded in annoyance. "It's being together that counts."

She had collapsed on the sofa then, too tired to say any more, and cried bitter tears of anger and frustration.

GOT it all planned, Mother?" Barry's voice cut into her memories. She gripped her handbag, feeling the metal clasp cold against her fingers. "I — I can't do it," she answered.

His eyes darkened. "Why not?"

"Rita and I are a generation and thousands of miles apart. Our tastes are different. They must be."

"Nonsense! She'll love anything you do."

"I'm sure she'd rather choose —"

"I see," he said shortly. "That mother-in-law joke isn't funny, is it? It's true.

"I thought you were different, that you'd remember how lonely you were when you came to England, and how much Grandma did for you — letting you have her house and furniture. She was always talking about it. I thought you'd try to make Rita feel wanted."

How much Mrs Fenton had done for her! Mary almost laughed aloud, but bit back the words that rushed to her lips.

Proudly she lifted her head and looked at him. He really believed she'd been happy in that awful house. She had been successful in one way, at least. The children had never suspected how she really felt.

"It isn't that, Barry," she began as she met his level gaze, saw the stubborn set of his jaw. Oh, he was so like Hugh! He'd never understand — never!

He didn't know what it was like sitting in uncomfortable silence during Mrs Fenton's visits. Not that the old lady actually said anything. Disapproval of Hugh's wife was the more caustic because it was unspoken.

But the scathing look in her darting, bird-like eyes at the children's table manners, at Mary's smart clothes, at the way she sometimes neglected the housework to take the boys for a romp in the park — oh, Mary could remember them all too well.

With words you could air emotions, sort things out. Yet how could words cure the harm that words might cause?

Barry drove her back to Fieldview, the country house Hugh and she had bought after their other two sons had been killed in a car accident. After that they couldn't bear to stay in a house that held so many memories — good and bad.

Gradually she and Hugh had drifted apart, living almost as strangers, two people who wanted more than anything in the world to speak to each other, but found they had no words to say. Barry's return home had lifted them out of their lethargy into a happier relationship and she was deeply thankful.

Now she was faced with this heart-rending problem. How could she furnish a house for a girl she didn't know, had never even seen?

No, she couldn't do it. She couldn't plunge Rita headlong into a situation that could only lead to bitterness.

That's what half her mind said. The other half wondered dully if she was thinking of Rita's happiness, or trying to excuse her own shortcomings.

"MOTHER'S going to decorate and furnish the cottage," Barry announced when they got in.

Hugh's face took on its familiar closed look, but his eyes regarded her doubtfully. "Is she?" he said at last.

"Yes. I had quite a time convincing her, but she's agreed at last."

"Will Rita approve?" Hugh asked slowly.

"Oh, yes. It will be so much easier for Rita when she gets here — save her all the fuss and bother. The cottage is old and dreary, not a bit like Rita. She's gay and —"

Barry's anxiety for Rita's happiness, his desire to make things easier for her, seemed right and praiseworthy on the surface. But did men ever learn anything about women?

Hugh's eyes flickered, his eyebrows lifted, but he remained silent.

Mary felt alone, rejected. She could read her husband's thoughts. After all, she herself had made it quite plain to him that he'd made a tragic mistake in not allowing her to decorate and furnish their first home in England.

Had it been the same with Hugh all those years ago? Had his concern for her happiness blinded him to the fact that no woman can furnish another's home with any hope of success? From the start she had thought of Mrs Fenton as a meddlesome, interfering old woman, and Hugh a dutiful son intent upon pleasing his mother.

Had she been wrong?

Had Mrs Fenton been genuinely concerned with her son's happiness? Had she agreed to help in the same way Mary herself had agreed?

She'd never know. How stupid she'd been, she thought. If only — if only Mrs Fenton was alive — I could tell her that at last I understand. But it was too late, too late. Oh, Hugh! Oh, Hugh! I've led you such a miserable existence!

Tears were very near the surface, she fled to her room and let them flow. As the sobs eased she saw herself in the mirror, the threads of grey hair, the heavy lids hooding her eyes.

Trembling, she lifted Barry's wedding photograph. Rita was a tall, slim girl with wide-apart eyes under brows pointed like a jay's cap. She was smiling up at Barry, radiant as only a bride can be.

What was she like, this girl? Did she sulk when she was crossed, or swim the stormy sea of matrimony with sure, strong strokes? Mary re-read several letters Rita had written. They spilled over the anecdotes of Barry and their small son. They were intelligent, well written, but told little of the girl's likes and dislikes.

What shall I do, she wondered. What shall I do?

The bedroom door opened, and Hugh came quietly to her side. "Well, dear, feeling better now?"

She sighed, bowing her head. "I don't know. I just don't know what to do. If I refuse Barry will get someone else to do it, and Rita will think I don't like her, that I didn't even try — "

"You'll do the right thing," Hugh said softly. "I know that." He drew her closer and kissed her cheek.

"Oh, Hugh!" she choked. "If only I'd had more sense! Your mother — !"

"You were too young to be wise, dear. But you have more understanding now. Do what you feel is best."

It was a long time since they had been so close to each other in thought. She knew this was his way of saying, "Don't make the same mistake my mother did."

FOR the next three weeks, she was busy dashing from shop to shop, borrowing wallpaper sample books, colour charts, and swatches of material. Two village handymen began stripping the walls of paper and paint.

UNITED NATIONS

After driving halfway across France in swimming costumes to combat the heat, we arrived at the airport with barely three minutes left to check in at the flight desk.

Hurriedly I slipped on a shirt and tie, grabbed my briefcase containing passports and flight reservations and dashed into the building.

But I forgot one little thing — my trousers!

MAD DOGS AND ENGLISHMEN . . .

How's this for an international get-together?

While hitch-hiking in France I was in a Frenchman's car when we drove into the back of a big German saloon.

No-one was hurt, but the insurance had to be dealt with. But in which language?

My driver spoke only French, the German's girlfriend understood English and I knew a little French.

The Frenchman spoke to me in French, I repeated it to the girl in English, and she, in turn, translated it into German.

It took two hours to complete — but we parted the best of friends!

The day before Rita's arrival, she took Mrs Miller, her daily, to do the tidying up.

"Well," that worthy remarked, shaking her tousled head and pursing her lips, "I wouldn't mind moving into this place myself!"

"I thought you'd like it," Mary said, pleased.

On the way to the airport, Barry was his gay, good-humoured self. Hugh, driving, didn't talk much.

She saw the appraising look in Rita's eyes as they met and kissed her quickly.

"I'm so happy you're going to live here," she said with warmth.

Rita smiled and relaxed as if she, too, had been dreading this meeting. Mary looked at Nigel, whose blond head was buried in Barry's shoulder. He peeked at her shyly with wondering blue eyes, then gave her a toothy grin.

"Would you like to have lunch first?" Mary asked. "And then go to the cottage? I hope you'll stay with us until you've settled in."

Barry laughed. "Mother has been busy fixing up the cottage. She wouldn't let even me see it. Saved it as a surprise for you!"

Mary could not look at Rita. She didn't want to see the alarm, the anger, she knew must be written on the girl's face.

Barry and Nigel seemed to be the only ones who ate lunch with any enjoyment, Afterwards, Barry put Nigel to bed in the spare room for his afternoon nap, and Hugh promised to baby-sit.

Almost apathetically, Rita stood for a moment in front of the newly-thatched cottage. The door hung straight and true now. The windows glistened in the bright sunlight. Even the chrysanthemums nodded gently in the breeze as if to say, "Welcome."

Barry inserted the key, threw open the door, and made to go in. Mary held him back.

"Let Rita go in alone," she begged, and her heart hammered against her ribs. Oh, let her be glad, she prayed. Please let her see what I tried to do.

"But —" Barry gave her a puzzled look, then stood back.

It was the longest five minutes Mary had ever lived through. Then suddenly Rita appeared at the door, her eyes shining, lips parted in a smile. She flung herself into Mary's arms.

"You did understand!" she exclaimed and began to cry.

"Well, for heaven's sake, what goes on?" Barry demanded.

He plunged into the cottage. A moment later he came out in a rush, looking exasperated. "But there's nothing there! Only bare walls, heaps of wallpaper samples, some little bits of fabric —"

"And a bowl of chrysanthemums," Rita said, flushed with happiness. "Oh, Barry, your mother is wonderful! She's had all the dirty work done. Now we'll have the fun of doing the rest ourselves." She turned to Mary, eager, alive, loving. "You'll help us, won't you, Mother?"

"Women!" Barry groaned, shaking his head. "I'll never understand them!"

"Don't try," Mary advised, turning with twinkling eyes to exchange a glance with Rita.

The End

"Is There A Patient In The House?"

There certainly is, says MARGARET BROWN. Except that "patient" is hardly the operative word . . .

A THIN cry somewhere in the dark recesses of the night.

I curl down deeper into the bedclothes.

Another cry.

A dream, I comfort myself, burying my head. Just a nasty old dream.

The cry resolves itself into a whining, "Mummy, I don't feel well."

No dream, this, and I slither out of bed and pad across the landing, bracing myself as my feet touch the icy linoleum. At the three doors facing me, I hesitate — which of them is it? A strangled gurgle comes from the centre one and I fling it open just in time to see my middle son being well and truly sick over everything.

Then begins the all too familiar pattern. Dump the unsavoury things in the bath; fumble in the linen cupboard, re-equip the bed; place a basin strategically at the bedside (I can't for the life of me think why, since none of my children has ever yet managed to aim into it) and finally stumble back to bed.

This process repeats itself at intervals throughout the night until the bath is full, the linen cupboard almost bare and my nerves distinctly jangly. Two minutes before the alarm goes off, my son finally sinks into a deep sleep. I stagger back to the bedroom just as my husband opens one eye,

153

smiles, and says lazily, "Good-morning, darling, sleep well?"

THE cause of all the trouble wakens around 10. Flushed and sleepy, he informs me his throat's sore, and his head aches and he doesn't think he should go to school. I telephone the doctor, search for clean sheets and hurry back to the patient. He's now wearing that angelic, i-haven't-got-long-to-go look which has terrified panicky mothers like me since time began.

I ask him for the tenth time how he feels and he shakes his head sorrowfully and points to this throat, indicating his inability to talk — a rarity, indeed. I feel quite guilty remembering all the thousands of times I've told him to be quiet.

Then I make the ridiculous mistake — and, heavens, I should know better by now — of putting a clapper bell on his table.

"Just ring it, darling," I hear myself say, "if you want anything."

His eyes open very wide. "I promise," he croaks.

He keeps his promise faithfully in the next half-hour by ringing vigorously every five minutes and asking , in a quavery whisper, for everything from, "Daddy's radio" to "just a little talk with you."

By noon his head's cooler and his eyes are brighter. Even his voice is gradually returning to its usual shrieking intensity . . . that is, until I poke my head round the door to see if he's in the throes of some mortal agony. Then his hand flutters weakly in the direction of his throat and he falls back on the mangled sheets.

The doctor gives him about another 70 years to live but adds I should keep him in bed for a day or two to be on the safe side. He looks at the boy's frail, still figure, "He doesn't look as if he wants to get up anyway, poor old chap."

I begin to tell him the poor old chap

just happens to be a very good actor and is, at that very moment, planning his next fiendish move.

The doctor looks searchingly at my bleary eyes and wan smile. He says I look a bit off colour myself and wouldn't I like him to give me a going-over?

I tell him there's nothing I want less just then than a "going-over" and I'm just tired.

"Must look after yourself and get plenty of sleep," he says as he charges down the garden path.

Very funny, I think, returning to my mountain of washing.

BY afternoon, the boy's cheeks have reverted to their usual, healthy pinkness, his sore throat appears to have undergone a speedy recovery and his mother is almost dead on her feet. I feel if I hear just one more version of "God Save The Queen" warbled to the music of the Rolling Stones' latest hit, I shall go stark, staring mad.

I give him comics — he wants to get up. I give him jigsaw puzzles — he wants to get up.

Next morning I decide to kill two birds with one stone by cleaning out his room, keeping an eye on him at the same time.

He says, "Can I watch? I've never even seen one bird killed before."

As I investigate the horrors lurking in his cupboards I'm amazed by the squirrel-like qualities of the human male animal.

I come across banana skins in the last vile stages of decomposition along with hundreds of crumpled bus tickets. I discover apple cores and foreign stamps, well-chewed-up pencils and half-chewed-up toffees, bottle tops and petrified fruit gums.

I come across a cardboard box, saying in large letters on the outside, "Privet — Very Secrit — Do Not Opin."

Under his smouldering gaze I

"opin" and find bits of wire, an old spring or two and the works of an ancient clock all knitted together with bits of string.

"I'm going to be an inventor and this is my first invention," he gasps, trying out the mattress as a trampoline.

This is it, I say to myself, and telephone the doctor. Bless him, he understands, and tells me I may let him up as long as I keep him warm and in the house for a day or two.

A FEW days later I visit a friend whose little girl has also caught this fleeting virus.

There she is, at three o'clock in the afternoon, sitting up in her spotless, white bed. Her covers come neatly to where covers ought to come, tight and tidy, and she smiles benignly at me, indicating the chair beside the bed.

It's the royal command to sit and talk a bit. She does the talking, of course, and occasionally, with great effect, she takes a tiny lacy-edged handkerchief and wipes her feverless brow.

It appears the doctor gave her the all-clear two days ago but, as her mother says, she's so much better behaved in bed that she's just leaving her there.

And they say there's only one little difference between the sexes!

The End.

WHAT OUR READERS SAID ON CHILDREN . . .

While I was reading our local evening newspaper, I came across the following advertisement:

HIGH PRAM. Hubcaps, white and navy with canopy, carefully driven by lady owner, never raced or rallied, low mileage, M.O.T. tested.

My friend, Susan, who has three lively children, was playing Cowboys and Indians with them when I called in for a visit.

As one of the boys levelled his toy gun at his mother and shouted, "Bang!" she slumped to the floor and lay still.

As I bent over anxiously she opened one eye and sighed. "Shhh. I always do this. It's the only chance I get to rest!"

"I don't like them standing up and I don't like them lying down," my three-year-old nephew said.

"Well," how do you like them?" I asked.

"Strangled," came the reply.

Fortunately he wasn't talking about his friends but about boiled, fried and scrambled eggs!

A friend's identical twin boys had just got new suits. Trying them on at home, one of the boys asked to be lifted up to see himself in the mirror.

"You don't have to see yourself in the mirror," his twin brother told him. "Just look at me. We're exactly the same!"

155

Lady, You've A Lucky Face !

Small consolation for
having any army
of tinkers,
tramps and hawkers who
looked on her lovely
house as their home from
home. . .

Complete Story
by Y. E. PETER

IT was such an ordinary house — no different from a hundred others in the district.

So why, Myra Evans wondered despairingly, did that decrepit-looking old man in the torn, filthy raincoat make straight for it with hardly a glance at any of the others?

"I thought you said tramps were a dying race, Barrie," she said.

Her husband looked up from the fireplace, where he was busy re-setting a loose tile.

"Hm? Did I? Well, I suppose they are. There can't be many down-and-outs these days with Social Security and everything."

His tongue appeared as he lined up the tile with perfect precision. The tongue business was essential to the completion of any job with Barrie.

The expected rat-tat came and Myra sighed.

"In that case," she retorted, "every tramp in Britain must have turned up at this house in the last two months."

She peeped round the edge of the window curtain. The old man was standing on the doorstep like a cast-off bundle of rags.

"They seem to home on the house, as if it's equipped with radar or something," she muttered. "You go, Barrie. And tell him we don't want anything."

Barrie stood up and dusted the knees of his old trousers.

"It's just as well I had a day off today," he said in his man-of-the-house voice. "There's no earthly reason why they shouldn't work for a living, the same as everyone else. Trouble is people are too soft with them."

He walked out into the hall and Myra heard him open the door.

He was back a moment later.

"That got rid of him," he said. But he wasn't quick enough stowing away the grubby white envelope.

Myra crept up behind him as he knelt down at the fireplace and delved into his pockets.

"Got it!" she said, sniffing at the contents. "Lavender! I might have known."

Barrie looked sheepish. "Well, it was only ten pence. And the poor devil looked as if he hadn't got the price of a meal on him."

Myra snorted. "There must be an awful lot of starving people in this neck of the woods then. Look!"

She dug into the depths of the old-fashioned porcelain fruit bowl.

"Imitation violets. A sprig of white heather. *For luck, dearie!* Lavender. A scent card. A tin opener that won't work. More lavender!"

She waved the scent card under Barrie's nose. *"Keep you linen fresh, dearie!"*

Barrie recoiled, screwing up his face. "It stinks! Put it on the fire!"

"The whole lot can go on the fire," Myra decided, scooping up the articles. "I don't know why I didn't do it in the first place."

In the doorway she turned, puzzled, to

face her husband. "But why, Barrie?" she asked. "Why do they pick on this house?"

"They don't. They go from door to door. There's nothing special about us!"

"They don't, you know. I've watched them and I can tell you they don't call at any of the others."

"Rubbish! Don't tell me you stand looking out of the window all day, to see who's coming," Barrie scoffed. "Anyway, if it worries you, I'll get a plate to stick on the gateposts. One of those 'no hawkers' affairs.

"Oh, and that reminds me — the gatepost is a bit rocky, I'll have to fix that, too."

Barrie already had a list as long as his arm of things to repair or rebuild round the house.

They'd got the place for a ridiculously low figure because Mrs Littleton, the old lady who'd owned it, had let it go for years.

When she'd died, the house had been the only thing of value in her whole estate.

After putting up with furnished flats for years Myra and Barrie had snapped it up.

It was Myra's first experience of being a real housewife. Because she was expecting a baby in the autumn, Barrie had refused to let her take on a job here, even a part-time one.

F OR the next week or so, Myra wasn't bothered quite so frequently by the "gentleman of the road" or by swarthy women with huge market baskets. The "no hawkers" plate seemed to be working.

Nevertheless, hardly a day went by without somebody banging at the knocker when she was least expecting it.

Then there was a woman who asked if the Evans would put a poster in their window advertising a Whist Drive for the benefit of the Over-Sixties' Club.

"Mrs Littleton was such an enthusiastic member of the club," she said. "She always put a poster in her window. Of course, I realise she isn't here any more, but if you wouldn't mind . . ."

Myra didn't mind, so the poster duly appeared.

There were other things, too.

A middle-aged woman knocked at the door, carrying a cat in her arms. She was Mrs Whitworth from number twenty-two and she was going away for the weekend and had to leave Oscar.

"I know you're a comparative newcomer and it's rather a cheek when we don't know one another very well, but would you, could you please look after the cat and feed him? He's used to coming in and out of Mrs Littleton's . . ."

Barrie eyed the fat cat grumpily when he came in from work.

"You needn't worry," Myra said. "He's not stopping for long. Only until Monday. He's a weekend guest."

"Mmm." Barrie looked far from enthusiastic. "Still, it won't affect me much. I'll be spending my time on all the jobs that still need doing. I really must get down to that gatepost tomorrow."

In the end Barrie discovered the kitchen window needed re-puttying, a broken tile on the garage roof needed replacing, and a completely new valve was the only way to stop the water tank overflowing. And so the gatepost was left untouched, slightly askew on its base.

ON Monday evening Mrs Whitworth came to collect her cat, and shortly afterwards a very small Cub Scout knocked at the door and asked for the key to the Scout hut.

"Just what's going on?" Barrie demanded, coming into the hall and overhearing the little boy's garbled explanation. "We don't have a key and never have as far as I know."

The small Cub looked a bit taken aback and glanced out to the road where a Scout and another Cub were hanging on to the handle of a cart loaded with jumble.

The older boy hurried up the path to help out.

"Mrs Littleton had a key to the hut, sir," he said in a business-like way. "The ASM says it wasn't returned, so we wondered if you still had it. We've been collecting for the jumble sale next Saturday, but the cart's full. We thought we'd dump some of it and then make another round of calls before we pack up for the evening."

"But why Mrs Littleton?" Barrie asked. "This house isn't the nearest to the hut, by a long chalk. Don't tell me she was a Cub?"

The heavy humour was lost on the earnest young man.

"No, sir. But she used to be an Akela, so she was always willing to do something for the group. She used to help out at garden fetes and things. I suppose you don't know where the spare key is now, sir?"

Barrie looked at Myra. "Do we?"

Suddenly she remembered. "There was an odd-looking key on the bunch the house agents gave us. I could never discover what it fitted and there's no label on it. Perhaps that's it."

It was. And the upshot of it was that Myra agreed to keep it permanently at the house for the Scouts when needed.

ON the Tuesday, Myra had just come back from a shopping trip and was upstairs taking off her coat in the front bedroom when she caught sight of the gipsy woman. She had a gaudy silk scarf knotted round her shoulders and a full-skirted dress sweeping round her ankles.

She was a few doors away, walking with a lithe unhurrying gait, and on her arm was a big basket.

Myra watched her approach, wondering if she'd go to any of the other houses. But she came steadily on until she was level with their gatepost.

She paused for a moment, studying the notice forbidding hawkers and canvassers, then she boldly pushed open the gate and walked in.

Myra decided to be out.

The woman knocked and went on knocking at intervals until Myra got so tired of standing like a dummy in the middle of the bedroom she resigned herself to answering the door.

"I don't want anything today . . ." she began firmly.

But the gipsy ignored her, swung her hawker's basket up to her knee and rested it there, going through her patter in a flat sing-song.

Her black eyes glittered in a way that made Myra a little afraid.

One end of the basket was packed with bunches of primroses.

Myra relented. "Oh, well — I'll take a bunch of flowers, please."

"Pegs, lady? Good strong pegs. They won't come apart, dearie."

"No. Really, I —"

"Lace, lady. Fine lace. Pretty for a baby's gown. And baby ribbon."

"Well, I don't think . . ."

How did she know?

"Take a blue ribbon, dearie. For a boy. And pins. Good strong pins. Guarded ends, look. You'll need plenty of pins."

The patter came to an end as Myra dug into her purse.

"Have you a cup of water, dearie? My throat's parched."

Myra was glad to escape and went to fetch it. The woman drank it down in deep, satisfying draughts.

"You've a kind face, lady," she said as she handed back the glass with a nod of thanks. "I see a long life and happiness for you. And lots of luck. It'll be a fine boy baby and bring joy to its mother, dearie."

Myra met the unfathomable Romany eyes and felt oddly pleased. This woman must have second sight, she thought. I don't even show, yet . . .

"Thank you very much," she managed to say. And then, as the woman swung her basket up on her arm, she plucked up courage to ask: "Why did you come here and not to the other houses?"

The woman turned and looked down the path before replying. When she spoke, it was in the same quaint sing-song.

"Your house is marked, with the sign of the travelling people, dearie. It says *Kind people live here. Travellers welcome!* God bless you, dearie."

K IND people live here," Myra said to herself. It sounded good. When the woman was out of sight, she went down to the gate and studied the gatepost, half-expecting to see the words carved on it. But there was nothing on it that meant anything to her.

Small boys' penknives had made cuts and slashes. One or two crude initials adorned it, a rough triangle, a circle with a hole dug out of the middle, a badly-shaped figure three.

Ordinary people, passing the post, wouldn't give it a second look. To them it would be just another gatepost.

Myra looked up and down the road and felt a glow of pride. She owned a gatepost, mysteriously and secretly different from all the rest. She couldn't let Barrie tear it up . . .

*   *   *   *

"You know, darling," Barrie said that evening, "it's not just the gipsies and tramps who home on this place. Look at all the other folk who've turned up on our doorstep in the last few weeks. We've never had time to feel strange or new and we've made a lot of friends."

Myra went and sat on the arm of his chair, feeling his arm close about her.

"And we're going to make a lot more," she said. 'Thanks to Mrs Littleton . . ."

The End.

A T least I think I would if I knew what people really were. All I really know about is my mother. And I like her even better than a saucer of milk. (Besides who needs a saucer of milk when Mum's around?)

I'm not sure I like being a kitten. Strange objects — ever so huge and high they are — keeping swooping down on me with sounds of "Oooh!" and "Ah!" and "He's so *cute*!"

And suddenly I feel myself *flying*! Yes, really! Flying! How else could I get so high off the ground?

It's not much fun being a kitten. You have such a small tummy . . . you no sooner start a meal than you have to finish — or burst. Mummy eats and eats and eats. I wish I was grown up . . .

I don't really live in this bag. I just climbed in to try it for size . . . and to make sure it was empty. I like climbing into things. Especially warm places where you curl up and sleep for ages. (I could sleep longer if I had a bigger tummy and didn't have to wake up to eat.)

I don't like being bossed. And Mummy bosses me all the time. "Wash your face!" . . . "Clean your ears!" . . . "Lick your coat!" . . . "It's time you went outside!"

There's one thing I wanted to ask . . . oh yes! Tell me, what are people? Is there enough liver and fish and milk for them, too? And do they have big tummies?

OCCUPATIONAL HAZARDS
What's that mean?

MOTTO
Food for thought.

I LIKE PEOPLE

ALL night long, the wind swept down the loch in blustering fury, twisting trees and driving sleet against the hills.

But with the approach of dawn the storm began to die and mist crept in, shrouding the landscape.

Slowly, through the filtering light, the cottage on the lochside took shape. Small, grey, desolate-looking; it might well have been deserted.

Inside, Helen McIntosh lay watching the coming of day as she had watched the slow passing of the night. She rose wearily and dressed.

Moving quietly, she started a fire going and put the meal to cook slowly. No need to waken Hamish so early. The boy had a long day ahead.

She made her bed, then dragged the old suitcase from beneath and lifted it on to the covers to check the contents for the last time. The last time . . .

Tears pricking at her eyelids made it difficult for her to see, but she knew what was there by heart.

Silently she turned away and stood looking round the little kitchen, seeing nothing. A band of pain encircled her head, making it difficult for her to think and the feeling of being stifled rose as the room seemed to close in on her.

She lifted her coat from behind the door to go out for a breath of air. As she slipped it on, she saw the wrapping paper that had contained the watch lying on the floor. Hamish had dropped it there in his excitement the night before.

Her breath caught in her throat as she bent to pick it up.

"You bought it for me?" he'd said, incredulously, to Colin Fraser. "A watch . . . for me?" His eyes had shone with delight as he stammered his thanks. But more than that. More . . .

Unexpected jealousy had swept her like a wave as she looked from one to the other and sensed suddenly the bond that lay between Hamish

Complete Story by CATHERINE ARMSTRONG

Just One Word Of Love

He was her only son and she might never see him again. Yet when she'd said goodbye there was nothing else to be said.

and his schoolmaster. They were almost like father and son. Almost.

She hadn't realised . . . but then, how could she? When did she ever see them together?

Colin Fraser hadn't set foot in the house for years, until last night. Oh, he'd been her husband's friend, of course, but after Duncan's death, what had she wanted with friends?

Duncan had been her whole life — his friends only reminded her of her lost happiness. Like the others, Colin hadn't understood and like the others she'd driven him away.

No-one understood. No-one could help . . .

She screwed and twisted the crumpled wrapping paper, remembering the things Colin had said after the funeral.

Accept it, he'd urged her. *Of course you must grieve, but don't forget the boy . . . Think of Hamish. You have him to live for!*

A pious humbug, she'd called him, an interfering busybody . . .

Her face twisted at the memory. None of it was true. Colin was a good enough man, but what did *he* know of what she'd lost? How could *he* even begin to imagine what she and Duncan had shared?

WITH slow, fumbling fingers she started to fasten her coat.

Oh, there had been love in her then. Love overflowing. For Duncan, for Hamish. She looked at the door of Hamish's bedroom and thought of him still sleeping there.

What love had Hamish known those last few years? What had she given him apart from a bed to sleep in, food to eat . . . ?

In her heart she had resented him: his eagerness for life; his boy's forgetfulness of tragedy.

He'd forced his way between her and her grief until she'd longed for him to grow up and be gone. The life he'd brought to the house was no part of her life . . .

It's A Man's World!

WHY are boys so big?

"You're nothing but a baby!" he keeps telling me.

He won't walk down the same street with me. If he *has* to he walks on the opposite pavement.

He does make life so difficult! I wish he wasn't so good looking in that lean and hungry way. When he's moody, he's magnificent. And when he's magnificent, I feel all sloppy.

Like now. I was sitting in my back garden, minding my own business and doing nothing in particular except demolish this lovely, whopping ice-cream cone . . . when he peers over the fence from his back garden and spots me.

"Hello, beautiful," he says.

I look round but there's nobody else there but me.

"Yes." He nods solemnly. "You get more beautiful every day. Honestly, I mean it! You'll be in films or on the telly before you know what's what!"

He's not only good looking, but so intelligent.

"Would you like a lick of my ice-cream cone?" I say.

He doesn't answer, because he's already grabbed it before I finish speaking and he's giving my ice-cream big licks.

That is when I get so bothered about him being so much bigger than me. His tongue is so huge! It takes an awful lot of ice-cream off with every slurpy lick!

Maybe I don't love him so much as I thought. 'Cos if you love someone, you're supposed to give them anything they want — but I'm not giving him all my ice-cream.

He gives it back to me very rudely. "When I said you would be in films," he said, "I meant horrible films!"

And stalks off.

Aren't men funny creatures? Fancy not knowing a simple word like "horrific"!

But now that day had come, and instead of relief and gladness thoughts she had put behind her for years came flooding in, bringing remorse.

Her hands rose wearily in an unthinking gesture to her brow and she moved to the door.

Outside the air was chill and damp and the mist clung wetly to her cheeks and hair, calming the confusion in her mind.

She climbed swiftly along the little path that led to the headland overhanging the loch; the path she alone had made.

The wind plucked savagely at her skirt as she reached the top. Momentarily she felt elated, responsive to the wildness around her.

She stood on the edge of the crumbling cliff looking down at the cold grey waters of the loch.

This was where Duncan's boat had been found that night four years ago and, the following day, Duncan himself . . .

Duncan, her husband.

164

She stood, shoulders hunched against the cold, staring intently down at the bay. Around her a curlew swooped and curved unnoticed.

Suddenly she turned, and without a backward glance sped quickly down the path.

H AMISH was already up when she got back. He was washing at the sink. He turned his head.

"Good morning, Mother."

She nodded briefly. "You get dressed. I'll see to the breakfast."

She studied him furtively as he stood splashing the icy water over his face and chest and up his thin, muscular arms.

He's grown, she thought. I hadn't noticed. He is beginning to look like Duncan.

Her breath caught in her throat as she watched him cross the kitchen and go into his room. He even walks like my Duncan now, she thought incredulously. Had he grown up overnight, or was it that she had refused to see him?

She could keep him, she thought suddenly. She could keep him yet. One word, that was all, One word, and he would stay.

She could see the years rolling over them, bringing them closer and closer together until at last they could share an unspoken thought — feel warm and safe in each other's company. As she and Duncan had done . . .

But he wasn't Duncan. He was her son. He deserved better than that. He deserved everything Colin Fraser was offering.

She felt the almost-forgotten well of love rise, and she could have wept; for Hamish; for herself; for the lost years. But there was no time for weeping now. That was all it would take to make him doubt the step he was taking.

HAMISH came back into the kitchen, fully dressed, and began laying the table. He moved quietly from cupboard to table, whistling softly under his breath.

He's nervous, she thought. And excited, yet trying hard not to show it.

"Sit in," she said, bringing his breakfast to the table. She poured herself a cup of tea and sat down facing him.

"You won't be sorry to get away from here, Hamish," she said.

He blushed and looked at her uncertainly.

"Oh, I don't know about that, Mother," he said hesitantly. "But this is a great chance for me. There's little for me in the village . . ."

He was watching her intently.

"No, you're right. There's nothing for you here." She spoke in a level, expressionless voice. "Nothing."

Hamish looked back at his plate. "You know, I'm lucky, Mother. Going to America, I mean — I'm getting a marvellous chance. And I — I'll be able to send for you soon."

It was a marvellous chance, she could see that. She'd driven him to Mr Fraser, but the schoolteacher hadn't let him down.

"I want to help the lad," he'd said. "He'll have to work. But if he does, I promise I'll send him to my brother in America. He will be glad to have a well-doing lad like Hamish. He will help him get on his feet."

HAMISH pushed aside his plate, the food unfinished. She saw him look at his wrist-watch and smile. It seemed like a symbol of the glittering future when all would be put right.

"Mother," he blurted out, "how am I ever going to repay Mr Fraser for all he has done for me?"

"Repay? Repay Colin Fraser?" She crumbled the bread nervously between her fingers. "Only by working, Hamish. He's got a lot of faith in you.

"Work — and be happy," she went on. "That's all the payment he would want."

She saw the red, boyish hands clutch convulsively on the cup he was holding. She could have wept and flung her arms around him, begging his forgiveness.

"You have your tickets? You have your money safe?" She could scarcely form the words, and knew her anxiety made her sound abrupt.

"Don't worry, Mother. I can look after myself. I'm not a boy!"

Not a boy! Oh, Hamish!

She lifted her eyes from the table and looked at him. Now she could say something real — something that would make things different, before it was too late. She opened her mouth, not knowing what the magic words would be, but Hamish sprang to his feet. His quick, expectant ears had caught the sound of the car.

"There's Mr Fraser now, Mother. I mustn't keep him waiting."

He dashed into the bedroom for his coat and caught up the suitcase on his way out. At the door he stopped, suddenly unsure, boyish.

"Well, Mother, I must be off." He took a half step towards her and for the first time she could see a glint of moisture in his eyes.

"Goodbye, Hamish lad," was all she said. "Write."

He stood looking at her hesitantly, and suddenly, uncontrollably, his mouth trembled.

She knew then he was waiting for her to kiss him, to show him it mattered that he was going away.

Her body ached to go to him, but she knew it was a selfish, negative love . . .

"Yes, I'll write, Mother," he said softly, and went slowly, miserably, down the path.

He fumbled for a second at the gate and his hand flew to his eyes. Then he was running towards the car and the patient, solid figure of the schoolmaster sat watching.

As he reached the car he turned and looked back at the cottage.

It was then she allowed herself one small gesture. Just a wave of her hand. "Goodbye, son," she said softly.

The End.

AS OTHERS SEE US . . .

What a many-sided person I am.

To the shops I am a customer; to the bank a depositor; to the electricity board a consumer; to the railways a passenger.

The hospital regards me as a patient and the income tax department as a taxpayer. I am a client to my lawyer, a voter to my MP, a householder to the council . . .

But to my own family, I'm just Mum — and that's the one I like best.

✳   ✳   ✳   ✳

I'm unmarried, but whenever a salesman knocks at my door I acquire a husband.

He varies according to the goods I'm asked to buy. If the blankets are narrow and short, then he's a large man who likes the bedclothes pulled over his ears.

He can also be very mean and is likely to turn quite violent if I spend money on unnecessary brushes and polishes. And I simply can't buy flowers because they give him hay fever.

He's a most versatile man, this husband of mine — and I wouldn't be without him!

SAILOR AHOY!

Launch out on this novel toy design for our sailor boy.
He'll make a splendid playmate for the beautiful rag
doll we featured earlier.

Materials Required. — For doll — Of **Lister-Lee Richmond Double Knitting containing Bri-Nylon**, 5 x 50 gram balls Cream (Pearl Oyster), 4 x 50 gram balls Black. For the clothes — 2 x 50 gram balls Light Navy, 3 x 50 gram balls Arctic White. One pair each 3¼ mm and one odd (if possible) and 3¾ mm (Nos. 10 and 9) knitting needles; large-eyed darning needle; stuffing; odd lengths of red and blue yarn for features; elastic for breeches, hat and jumper; 4 small buttons; about ½ yard Vilene or any stiff material; 1 press fastener; piece of white lining for hat.

For best results it is essential to use the recommended yarn. If you have difficulty in obtaining the yarn, write direct, enclosing a stamped addressed envelope, to the following address for stockists: Lister-Lee Knitting Wools and Yarns, George Lee & Sons Ltd., P.O. Box 37, Whiteoak Mills, Wakefield, Yorkshire WF2 9SF.

Abbreviations. — St.-st. — stocking-stitch; P — purl; st.(s) — stitch(es); K — knit; tog. — together; cm — centimetres; mm — millimetres; y.o.n. — yarn over needle; y.f. — yarn forward; sl. — slip; g.-st. — garter-stitch; N — Navy Blue, W — White; C — Cream; B — Black; p.s.s.o. — pass slipped stitch over.

Tension. — 24 sts. and 34 rows to 10 cm, *4 inches,* over st.-st. using single yarn and 3¾ mm needles.

TO MAKE DOLL
Legs.

Using 3¼ mm needles and C double, cast on 42 sts. and work in st.-st. for 13 cm, *5 inches,* ending with a purl row.

Work 2 rows purl to form stitching line (knee joint). Continue in st.-st. for 4 rows.

Next row.—Decrease 1st. each end. Work 9 rows.

Break off C, join in B double (for boots).

Repeat last 10 rows 5 times more. (30 sts.)

Work 4 rows.

Next row. — K20, turn. P10, turn, K10.

Work 21 more rows on these 10 sts., end with a purl row.

Break yarn, leave sts. on needle. With right side of work facing, commencing where 10 sts. were left and using same needle, rejoin yarn and knit up 12 sts. evenly along side of instep, knit across first 5 sts. on needle, with odd 3¼ mm needle knit the other 5 sts., pick up 12 sts. along other side of instep, knit remaining 10 sts.

Working with 3 needles, purl across all sts., counting all sts. as 1 row. Continue in st.-st. for 4 more rows.

Next row. — *K1, K2 tog., K21, K2 tog., K1, repeat from * once more.

Next row. — P22, P2 tog., P2, P2 tog., purl to end.

Next row. — K8, turn, P8.

Cast off 8 sts., join yarn to remaining sts., K1, K2 tog., K26, K2 tog., K1, turn, P1, P2 tog., P24, P2 tog., P1. Cast off.

Join yarn to remaining 8 sts. Work 2 rows. Cast off.

Make 2nd leg to match.

Arms.

With 3¼ mm needles and C double, cast on 4 sts. and knit one row.

2nd row. — Purl, increasing 1 st. at each end.

Continue in st.-st. increasing 1 st. at each end of every row until there are 30 sts. on the needle.

Continue straight until work measures 10 cm, *4 inches,* ending with a purl row.

Next row. — K13, (K2 tog.) twice, K13.

Purl one row.

Next row. — K12, (K2 tog.) twice, K12.

Purl one row.

Next row. — K12, K2 tog., K12.

Continue without shaping until work measures 18.5 cm, *7¼ inches,* ending with a purl row.

Thumb.

1st row. — K12, pick up loop between sts. and knit into back of it, K1, pick up loop, knit into back of it, knit to end.

Work 3 rows.

Repeat these 4 rows twice more, but work 3 sts., then 5 sts. between pick-up loops.

Next row. — As 1st row but work 7 sts. between loops. (33 sts.)

Next row. — P20, turn, K7, turn, P7, turn, K7, then cast off the 7 sts.

Join yarn on purl side in middle of row, purl to end.

Continue on 26 sts. in st.-st. for 3 cm, *1¼ inches,* ending with a purl row.

Cast off 2 sts. at beginning of next 2 rows. K2 tog. at each end of the next 4 rows. Cast off.

Make second arm to match.

Front Body.

With 3¼ mm needles and C double, cast on 39 sts. Work in st.-st. for 11 cm, *4½ inches.* Decrease 1 st. at each end of the next row. Work 3 rows.

Decrease 1 st. each end of the next row. Work 1 row.

Increase at each end of the next row. Work 3 rows.

Increase each end of the next row. Work straight until body measures 26.5 cm, *10½ inches.*

Shape Shoulders.

Cast off 4 sts. at beginning of next 4 rows. Work 4 rows.

Head.

Next row. — Increase 1 st. at each end.

Next row. — Purl.

Repeat these two rows until there are 39 sts. on the needle.

Continue straight for 9 cm, *3½ inches.*

Next row. — K2 tog., K16, sl.1, K2 tog., p.s.s.o., K16, K2 tog.

Next row. — Purl.

Repeat these 2 rows, working 2 sts. less between decreases, 3 times more. (23 sts.)

Next row. — K19, turn, P15, turn, K11, turn, P7, turn, knit to end.

Next row. — Purl. Cast off.

Make another body piece the same for the Back, but change to B for back of head after increases, when there are 39 sts. on needle.

To Make Up.

Press pieces lightly with a warm iron over a dry cloth.

Stitch boot and leg seams, turn to right side. Stuff boot and leg up to stitching line with seam at back, back stitch through line.

Now continue to stuff leg to within 1 cm, *⅜ inch,* of top, stitch cast-on edges together.

Stitch thumb and arm seams, turn to right side. Stuff hand flat for 4 cm, *1½ inches,* then stitch three lines to indicate fingers. Stuff remainder of arm. Stitch cast-on edges together.

Stitch sides of body and head together, leaving a space to insert arms and legs and leaving top open. Turn to right side. Stitch arms and legs to body. Stuff body and head firmly.

Work face as in picture, using black yarn for the outline of the eyes and eyebrows, blue for the eyes, and red for the lips and nose.

Hair.

Mark a thin pencil line from end of increases each side, sloping slightly down at back of neck. Cut B into lengths of 10 cm, *4 inches,* and threading 3 strands through darning needle, starting just in front of side seams, take up about 2 sts., and with yarn even, tie knot.

Continue in this way across to other side. Repeat this row about 2 cm, *¾ inch,* apart until top seam is reached, the work 1 row in front of seam for fringe.

BREECHES
Right Leg.

Using 3¼ mm needles and N single, cast on 54 sts.

1st row. — K2, *P2, K2, repeat from * to end.

2nd row. — P2. *K2, P2, repeat from * to end.

Work 1st row once more.

4th row. — *P2, y.o.n., K2 tog., repeat from * to last 2 sts., P2

Work 1st and 2nd rows once more.

7th row. — K10, turn, purl back.

Repeat 7th row, working an extra 10 sts. each time until K40, turn, purl back.

Next row. — Knit across all sts., increasing 1 st. each end.

Work 5 rows st.-st.
Repeat last 6 rows 7 times more. (70 sts.)
Next row. — Mark each end with odd yarn for crotch.
Continue in st.-st. without shaping for 14 cm, *5½ inches.****
Next row. — K34, turn, (P2 tog.) to end of row. Work on these 17 sts. for 12 rows in g-st. Cast off.
With right side facing, join yarn to remaining 36 sts. and knit to end.
Next row. — (P2 tog.) to end. (18 sts.)
Next row. — Cast on 5 sts., knit to end.
Knit one row.
Next row. — K2, y.f., K2 tog. (buttonhole made), knit to end.
Knit 7 rows.
Repeat buttonhole row.
Knit one row. Cast off.

Left Leg.
Work as Right Leg until ribbing is finished, then knit 1 row.
Next row. — P10, turn, knit to end.
Repeat last row, working an extra 10 sts. each time.
Continue as Right Leg as far as ***.
Next row. — K36, turn, (P2 tog.) to end of row.
Next row. — K18, turn, cast on 5 sts., knit to end.
Next row. — Knit to last 3 sts., y.f., K2 tog., K1
Knit 7 rows.
Repeat buttonhole row.
Knit one row.
Cast off.
With right side facing, join yarn to remaining 34 sts. and knit one row.
Next row. — (P2 tog.) to end. (17 sts.)
Work 12 rows in g.-st.
Cast off.

To Make Up.
Stitch legs up to crotch marks, then join front and back of breeches. Thread elastic through holes and sew buttons on to legs to match buttonholes.

JUMPER
Back.
With 3¾ mm needles and W single, cast on 72 sts.

Beginning with a knit row, work 5 rows in st.-st., then knit 1 row to mark hemline.
Beginning with a knit row, continue in st.-st. for 5 cm, *2 inches,* ending with a purl row. Decrease 1 st. each end of next row.
Work 7 rows.
Repeat the last 8 rows 3 times more. (64 sts.)

Shape Armholes.
Cast off 3 sts. at beginning of next 2 rows.
Work 2 rows.
Next row. — K8, K2 tog., knit to last 10 sts., K2 tog., K8.
Work 5 rows.
Next row. — K7, K3 tog., knit to last 10 sts., K3 tog., K7.
Work 5 rows.
Repeat last 6 rows once more.
Cast off 5 sts. at beginning of next 4 rows.
Cast off remaining 28 sts.

Front.
Work as Back until 3rd decrease has been worked. (66 sts.)
Work 7 rows after decrease.
Next row. — K2 tog., K29, K2 tog., turn, leave remaining sts. on spare needle.
Work 7 rows, K2 tog. at neck edge on every knit row.
Next row. — Cast off 3 sts., knit to last 2 sts., K2 tog.
Work 3 rows, still decreasing at neck edge on knit row.
Next row. — K8, K2 tog., K11, K2 tog.
Work 5 rows, still decreasing at neck on every knit row.
Next row. — K7, K3 tog., K7, K2 tog.
Work 5 rows, decreasing at neck edge as before.
Next row. — K7, K3 tog., K2, K2 tog.
Next row. — Purl.
Next row. — K9, K2 tog.
Work 3 rows.
Cast off 5 sts. at beginning of next row.
Purl 1 row, then cast off remaining 5 sts.

With right side facing, join yarn to remaining 33 sts., K2 tog., knit to last 2 sts., K2 tog. Now complete to correspond with other side, reversing shaping.

Sleeves (Both Alike).

With 3¾ mm needles and W single, cast on 36 sts.

Knit one row.

Join N, knit 4 rows.

Knit 2 rows W.

Repeat last 6 rows once more, then 4 rows N.

Continue in st.-st. in W, increasing at each end of 7th row, then every 6th row until there are 46 sts.

Continue without shaping until work measure 16 cm, 6¼ inches, from beginning.

Cast off 3 sts. at beginning of next 2 rows, then 2 sts. at beginning of next 4 rows.

Cast off remaining 32 sts.

Join shoulder seams.

Collar.

With 3¾ mm needles and W single, cast on 40 sts. and work 5 cm, 2 inches, in st.-st. ending with a purl row.

Next row. — K7, cast off 26 sts., K7.

Continue on these 7 sts., decreasing 1 st. at inside edge on 8th row, then every 6th row until 2 sts. remain.

Work 1 row. Cast off.

With wrong side of work facing, join yarn to remaining 7 sts. Work to match other side.

With right side of work facing and N, pick up and K53 sts. along outside edge, 39 sts. across cast-on edge and 53 sts. up other side.

Next row. — K53, knit twice into next st., K37, knit twice into next st., K53.

Next row. — With W, K53, knit twice into next st., K39, knit twice into next st., K53.

Next row. — With W, K53, knit twice into next st., K41, knit twice into next st., K53.

Continue in 2 rows of alternate colours, increasing at corners in every row as before, until 3rd band of white has been worked. Cast off.

Front Piece.

With 3¾ mm needles and W single, cast on 38 sts. Knit 4 rows.

Next row. — K4, P30, K4.

Next row. — Knit.

Repeat these 2 rows until work measures 13 cm, 5 inches, ending with a wrong-side row.

Next row. — K11, cast off 16 sts. K11. Work on these sts.

Next row. — K4, purl to end.

Next row. — K2 tog., knit to end.

Repeat last 2 rows 5 times more.

Cast off remaining 5 sts.

With wrong side facing, join yarn to remaining sts. at neck edge, P7, K4.

Next row. — Knit to last 2 sts., K2 tog.

Complete to match other side.

With right side faceing and NB, pick up 13 sts. down side of neck, 16 sts. across Front, 13 sts. up other side.

1st row. — K12, K2 tog., K14, K2 tog., K12.

2nd row. — K11, K2 tog., K14, K2 tog., K11.

3rd row. — K10, K2 tog., K14, K2 tog., K10.

Cast off.

To Make Up.

Stitch collar round neck edge.

Sew in sleeves.

Join sleeve and side seams. Stitch one side of front piece inside shoulder seam. Stitch press fastener on other side. Turn up hem at bottom and sl.-st. Thread elastic through hem.

To Make Tie (make 2 pieces alike). — Cast on 7 sts. in N. Work 7.5 cm, 3 inches, in g.-st. K2 tog. at each end of next row.

Work 7.5 cm, 3 inches, in g.-st. Cast off.

To Make Bow. — Cast on 5 sts., work 3.5 cm, 1¼ inches, in g.-st. Fold narrow end of each tie to middle, making bow. Stitch small piece over middle, stitching at back, then on to front of jumper.

HAT

To make top of hat, cut a circle of Vilene or stiff material 14 cm, 5½ inches, in diameter. For band, cut a piece 43 cm, 17 inches, long by 4 cm,

Continued on page 174

I LIKE PEOPLE

ODD thing is, so few people like me.

All right, all right, so I don't exactly look like an advertisement for toothpaste. A chap can't help his looks!

Besides, we bloodhounds have a lot to be fed up about. Look at the way you people avoid us!

Would YOU have a bloodhound for a pet? Of course you wouldn't. Do you know anyone who would? 'Course you don't! You think of us only as howling our heads off at the end of a chain as we tear in pursuit of fugitives or convicts.

Actually we only do it because it's expected of us. We're really such friendly, lovable creatures.

We like to play just like other dogs. We're intelligent, charming, handsome — in a dignified sort of way — and very loyal.

What more could anyone ask for in a pet?

1½ inches, wide. Join ends of band and sew round circle, to make crown. Make brim (double if thin Vilene used) 28 cm, 11 inches, diameter. Mark inner circle 14 cm, 5½ inches, diameter, but cut inside 1 cm, ⅜ inch, that is 11.5 cm, 4½ inches, diameter. Cut slits down 1 cm, ⅜ inch, to mark, fit to crown by folding brim 1 cm, ⅜ inch, up outer side of crown.

***With 3¾ mm needles and N single, cast on 200 sts.

Knit one row.

2nd row. — *K18, K2 tog., repeat from * to end.

Continue in g.-st. in W decreasing every 3rd row, working 1 less st. between decreasings, until 100 sts. remain.***

Work 7 rows without shaping.

Next row. — **K8, K2 tog., repeat from ** to end.

Work 1 row without shaping.

Repeat last 2 rows, working one less st. between decreases until 20 sts. remain.

Work 1 row.

Next row. — (K2 tog.) to end.

Work 1 row.

Thread yarn through stitches, draw up and fasten off.

Join seam, stretch over top and down to edge of brim.

For under brim work as top brim, from *** to ***

Knit 2 rows.

Cast off.

Join seam. Stitch outer edge to outer edge of top brim, and cast-off edge to just inside band of crown. Stitch through navy, round edge of hat to keep lining and knitting together. Make inner lining in the same way as crown part of Vilene and stitch inside.

To Make Band.

Cast on 4 sts. in N and work 63 cm, 25 inches, in g.-st.

Stitch round crown, letting ends hang down back.

Make Bow. — Cast on 4 sts. Working in g.-st., one piece 20 cm, 8 inches, and one piece 4 sts., 4 cm, 1½ inches. Fold bow double, join at middle back. Stitch small piece over. Join to make knot. Stitch over join of band at back of hat. Stitch elastic each side to come under chin.

Too Rich To Day-Dream . . .

IT'S an old, old day-dream, isn't it — the game of "What would you do if you won a lot of money on the football pools?"

I suppose most of us have played it at one time or another!

The other day I met a man for whom the dream really came true. A few months back he had a fairly big win.

I asked him what difference it had made to his life. He looked at me and smiled.

"The only real difference is knowing that the money is there," he said.

"I haven't bought a new house or a new car, or even much for the house. We were quite happy before, and I reckon we wouldn't be any happier if we tried to change.

"I kept on my old job and stuck to the old routine. And you know what? Now that I know I can have lots of the things I used to want, somehow I don't want them any more."

I think I understand just how he feels. We, most of us, settle down to the kind of life we're made for, and we probably wouldn't be any happier in any other circumstances.

Only we tend to forget that sometimes, don't we? I suppose we'll always go on day-dreaming — hoping — yearning.

That's the way we're made. It's fun, too. I almost pity that man. He can't day-dream any more.